# STRATEGIES
# TO
# ACHIEVE
# READING
# SUCCESS

Book
# 4

CURRICULUM
ASSOCIATES®, Inc.

ISBN 0-7609-0697-1
©2000—Curriculum Associates, Inc.
North Billerica, MA 01862

15 14 13 12 11 10 9 8 7 6 5 4 3 2 1

# TABLE OF CONTENTS

## PART ONE: LEARN ABOUT MAIN IDEA

**Read this paragraph about wolves. As you read, think about the most important idea in the paragraph.**

### Howling Wolves

Wolves howl as a way to talk with one another. Wolves howl to stay in touch with their pack before, during, and after a hunt. And they howl to warn other wolf packs to keep out of their territory. Sometimes, wolves howl just for fun. When many wolves are howling at the same time, each wolf howls a different note. Heard together, the wolves sound like a group of singers.

The first sentence of the paragraph states the most important idea.

**Wolves howl as a way to talk with one another.**

The most important idea in a paragraph is called the **main idea.** The main idea tells what a paragraph is mostly about.

★ The main idea is sometimes found in the first sentence of a paragraph.

★ The main idea is sometimes found in the last sentence of a paragraph.

★ The main idea is sometimes not found in any one sentence. You can figure out the main idea by asking yourself, "What is the most important idea in the paragraph?"

Read this paragraph about bikes. As you read, think about the main idea of the paragraph. Then answer the questions.

### An Extraordinary Bike

Bikes have been around for more than 200 years. The first bikes weren't much fun to ride. Riders had to use their feet to push themselves along the ground. Then, in the 1870s, a bike called the ordinary appeared. The ordinary was different from the early bikes. It had pedals, handlebars, and brakes. It also had a huge front wheel and a tiny back wheel. Each full turn of the big wheel made the bike go farther. The seat was almost on top of the front wheel. So, getting on and off the ordinary was difficult. The rider also needed a lot of skill just to stay upright. Still, people enjoyed riding the ordinary. The ordinary soon became the first popular bike.

1. What is the main idea of the paragraph?
   Ⓐ The ordinary had a huge front wheel.
   Ⓑ Getting on and off the ordinary was difficult.
   Ⓒ The ordinary was the first popular bike.
   Ⓓ Riders used their feet to push the first bikes along.

2. Where or how did you find the main idea?
   Ⓐ in the first sentence of the paragraph
   Ⓑ in the last sentence of the paragraph
   Ⓒ in the middle of the paragraph
   Ⓓ by thinking about the most important idea in the paragraph

 Work with a partner. Talk about your answers to questions 1 and 2. Tell why you chose the answers you did.

**Remember: The main idea tells what a paragraph is mostly about.**

★ Read the first sentence of the paragraph. The main idea is sometimes found here.

★ Read the last sentence of the paragraph. The main idea is sometimes found here.

★ Sometimes, the main idea is not found in a sentence from the paragraph. You can figure out the main idea by thinking about the most important idea in the paragraph.

**Read this story about skateboarding. As you read, ask yourself, "What is the story mostly about?" Then answer the questions.**

### Surfing on Land

Sal was a surfer. He lived in California during the 1950s. Some days, the ocean waves weren't big enough to ride. Sal and his surfer friends had nothing to do. They got bored. Then, one day, Sal and the other surfers had an idea. They began nailing roller-skate wheels to narrow boards. They used these "skateboards" to "surf" on the street. Soon, skateboards were as popular as surfboards. But in skateboarding, no one ever got wet!

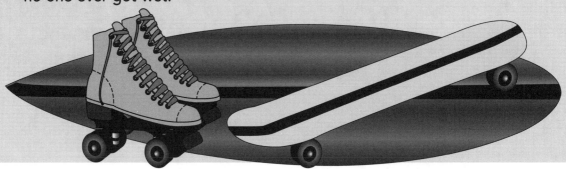

3. What is the story mostly about?
   Ⓐ Sal and his friends got bored easily.
   Ⓑ Surfers invented skateboarding in the 1950s.
   Ⓒ Sal was a surfer in California.
   Ⓓ Small waves are hard to surf.

4. Where or how did you find the main idea?
   Ⓐ in the first sentence of the paragraph
   Ⓑ in the last sentence of the paragraph
   Ⓒ in the middle of the paragraph
   Ⓓ by thinking about the most important idea in the paragraph

**Look at the answer choices for each question. Read why each answer choice is correct or not correct.**

3. What is the story mostly about?

   Ⓐ Sal and his friends got bored easily.
   *This answer is not correct because the only reason that Sal and his friends were bored was that the waves were too small to ride.*

   ● Surfers invented skateboarding in the 1950s.
   *This answer is correct because it tells what all the sentences in the story are mostly about. It is the most important idea.*

   Ⓒ Sal was a surfer in California.
   *This answer is not correct because it is one idea in the story, but it is not the most important idea.*

   Ⓓ Small waves are hard to surf.
   *This answer is not correct because, even though it is true that small waves are hard to ride, this idea is not what the story is mostly about.*

4. Where or how did you find the main idea?

   Ⓐ in the first sentence of the paragraph
   *This answer is not correct because the first sentence is "Sal was a surfer." This is not the most important idea in the paragraph.*

   Ⓑ in the last sentence of the paragraph
   *This answer is not correct because the last sentence is "But in skateboarding, no one ever got wet!" This is not the most important idea in the paragraph.*

   Ⓒ in the middle of the paragraph
   *This answer is not correct because the middle of the paragraph tells about how skateboards were made and used. Also, the main idea is more often found in the first or last sentence of a paragraph, not the middle.*

   ● by thinking about the most important idea in the paragraph
   *This answer is correct because the main idea is not found in the first sentence, the last sentence, or the middle of the paragraph. The main idea is found by thinking about what all the sentences in the paragraph are mostly about.*

★ Each paragraph in a reading passage has one main idea. Also, all the paragraphs together in a reading passage have one main idea. The main idea of a reading passage with two or more paragraphs is often found in the first or last paragraph.

★ The title of a reading passage tells something about the main idea.

**Read this report about a girl's camp experience. Then answer the questions.**

### When I Grow Up

I plan to become an astronaut when I grow up. This has been my dream ever since I read about Sally Ride. She was the first American woman in space.

This summer, I got the chance to experience what it's like to be an astronaut. I spent part of my vacation at a space camp for kids.

For six days, I got to do what an astronaut does. Part of my training included a "space mission." I worked with a team of other kids from all over the world. We took turns playing the roles of mission-control operators and of shuttle crew. I discovered what it feels like to be weightless and to spin in orbit. I also learned how difficult it is to do anything while wearing a space suit!

5. What is the main idea of the first paragraph?
   Ⓐ More women are becoming astronauts.
   Ⓑ A girl plans to become an astronaut.
   Ⓒ Sally Ride is a heroine to girls.
   Ⓓ Sally Ride was the first woman in space.

6. What is the main idea of the last paragraph?
   Ⓐ Kids from all over the world trained together.
   Ⓑ The girl got to spin in orbit.
   Ⓒ The girl discovered what it's like to be weightless.
   Ⓓ For six days, the girl did what an astronaut does.

7. What is the report mostly about?
   Ⓐ training for a space mission
   Ⓑ the first American woman in space
   Ⓒ a girl who wants to become an astronaut
   Ⓓ children who attended a space camp

8. Which of these is another good title for the report?
   Ⓐ "High Hopes for the Future"
   Ⓑ "The First Woman in Space"
   Ⓒ "Great Camps for Kids"
   Ⓓ "Mission Control"

**Read this fable from Aesop. Then answer the questions.**

A farmer's daughter had been out to milk the cows. She was returning to the dairy, carrying her pail of milk upon her head. As the milkmaid walked along, she began daydreaming.

"The milk in this pail will provide me with cream. I will make the cream into butter and take it to market to sell. With the money I make, I will buy a number of eggs. The eggs will hatch and produce a number of chickens. I shall sell some of my fowls, and with the money they will bring in, I will buy myself a new gown. I shall wear the gown when I go to the fair. All the young fellows will try to win my affection. But I shall toss my head and have nothing to say to them."

Forgetting all about the pail, the milkmaid acted out her last words and tossed her head. Down went the pail. All the milk was spilled, and all of her dreams vanished in the air.

9. What is the main idea of paragraph two?
   Ⓐ The cream from milk can be made into butter.
   Ⓑ The milkmaid would rather raise chickens than milk cows.
   Ⓒ The milkmaid dreams of all the things her milk will bring to her.
   Ⓓ The milkmaid likes fancy clothes.

10. The last paragraph is mostly about
    Ⓐ how the milkmaid's forgetfulness made her plans disappear.
    Ⓑ how the milkmaid acted selfishly.
    Ⓒ how mistakes happen to everyone.
    Ⓓ how the milkmaid worried that her father would be upset.

11. What is the fable mostly about?
    Ⓐ milk that vanishes into the air
    Ⓑ a girl who makes plans about things that haven't happened yet
    Ⓒ a daughter who behaves badly
    Ⓓ a milkmaid who wastes food

12. Which of these is the best title for the fable?
    Ⓐ "Spilled Milk"
    Ⓑ "The Farmer's Proud Daughter"
    Ⓒ "Don't Count Your Chickens Before They've Hatched"
    Ⓓ "Going to the Fair"

★ A test question about the main idea may ask you what a reading passage is *mostly* or *mainly* about.

★ A test question about the main idea may ask you to choose the best title for a reading passage. A good title tells something about the main idea of the whole reading passage.

**Here is a story about a spider named Legs. Read the story.
Then do Numbers 13 and 14.**

Legs was a trap-door spider who lived in a hole in the ground. The opening to his tunnel was a door made of dirt and silk. This trapdoor fit tightly over the opening, like a cork in a bottle. Every night, Legs would lift up the door and wait for his dinner. When an insect came near, Legs would run out and grab it.

Legs was mostly content, but one thing made him unhappy. He was tired of people's thinking that all spiders spin webs. Everyone was always praising the work of web-building spiders. Legs wished more people knew that some spiders, as he was, were brave hunters. After all, Legs didn't wait for food to enter his trap. He used his sharp eyes and fast legs to go after his meals. Legs hoped that someday his wish would come true and he would get the attention he deserved.

**Finding Main Idea**

13. The story is mostly about
    Ⓐ a spider who feels left out.
    Ⓑ a proud web builder.
    Ⓒ a spider who is never happy.
    Ⓓ a brave hunter.

**Finding Main Idea**

14. The best title for the story is
    Ⓐ "Entering a Trap."
    Ⓑ "One Wish."
    Ⓒ "Through a Trapdoor."
    Ⓓ "The Content Spider."

Here is an article about paper money in the United States. Read the article. Then do Numbers 15 and 16.

There are seven paper bills used for money in the United States today. These bills have values of $1, $2, $5, $10, $20, $50, and $100. On the front of each bill is the portrait of a great American. The faces of past presidents are printed on the $1, $2, $5, $20, and $50 bills. In order, these presidents are George Washington, Thomas Jefferson, Abraham Lincoln, Andrew Jackson, and Ulysses S. Grant.

Alexander Hamilton's face appears on the $10 bill. Ben Franklin's face appears on the $100 bill. Hamilton was the first Secretary of the Treasury. Franklin was a printer, an inventor, and a patriot.

Years ago, bills were printed with much higher values—$500, $1,000, $5,000, and even $10,000! These bills were not very popular, however. The government stopped printing them in 1969.

## Finding Main Idea

15. The article is mostly about
    - Ⓐ famous Americans.
    - Ⓑ the people whose faces appear on paper bills.
    - Ⓒ past presidents of the United States.
    - Ⓓ paper bills with high values.

## Finding Main Idea

16. Which of these is the best title for the article?
    - Ⓐ "A New Look for Paper Money"
    - Ⓑ "Great Presidents"
    - Ⓒ "Getting Your Face Known"
    - Ⓓ "Portraits on Bills"

## PART ONE: LEARN ABOUT FACTS AND DETAILS

Read this paragraph about animal names. The main idea is found in the first sentence. It is underlined for you. As you read, think about the sentences that tell more about the main idea.

**What's in a Name?**
Different terms are used to name male and female animals. On a farm, the chickens are roosters or hens. The horses are stallions or mares. The sheep are rams or ewes, and the pigs are boars or sows. In the woods, the deer and rabbits are bucks or does. Male elephants, whales, moose, and cattle are bulls, and the females are cows.

The sentences that tell more about the main idea are

**On the farm, the chickens are roosters or hens.**

**The horses are stallions or mares.**

**The sheep are rams or ewes, and the pigs are boars or sows.**

**In the woods, the deer and rabbits are bucks or does.**

**Male elephants, whales, moose, and cattle are bulls, and the females are cows.**

Sentences that tell more about the main idea are called **facts and details**. Facts and details explain or support the most important idea in the paragraph.

★ Facts and details provide information about the main idea.

★ Facts and details often tell about the *who, what, where, when, why,* and *how* of the main idea.

Read this paragraph about Michael. The main idea is found in the last sentence. It is underlined for you. As you read, think about the facts and details that tell more about the main idea. Then answer the questions.

### How Lucky Do You Feel?

Michael believes that doing certain things will bring him good luck. He always carries a rabbit's foot. He looks on the ground for pennies that are heads up. Sometimes, he even wears his clothes inside out. Michael also thinks that avoiding certain things can prevent bad luck. He won't walk under a ladder or open an umbrella indoors. And he'd never let a black cat cross his path. Michael's friends laugh at his strange beliefs, but he doesn't care. <u>Michael's superstitions make him feel safe</u>.

1. What is something that Michael believes will bring him good luck?
   Ⓐ walking under a ladder
   Ⓑ finding a penny heads up
   Ⓒ laughing a lot
   Ⓓ opening an umbrella indoors

2. Which detail tells why Michael always carries a rabbit's foot?
   Ⓐ He believes that doing certain things will bring him good luck.
   Ⓑ Sometimes, he even wears his clothes inside out.
   Ⓒ He won't walk under a ladder or open an umbrella indoors.
   Ⓓ His friends laugh at his strange beliefs, but he doesn't care.

 Work with a partner. Talk about your answers to questions 1 and 2. Tell why you chose the answers you did.

**Remember: Facts and details explain or support the main idea.**

★ Look for sentences that provide information about the main idea.

★ Look for sentences that tell about the *who, what, where, when, why,* and *how* of the main idea.

**Read this article about a fun sport. As you read, ask yourself, "What is the main idea? What facts and details tell *more* about the main idea?" Then answer the questions.**

### A Unique Game of Catch

Many people enjoy playing Frisbee. The sport costs very little. It can also be played almost anywhere outdoors.

Some students at Yale University invented this sport. The first Frisbee was a metal pie pan. Its original spelling was *frisbie*. It was named after the Frisbie Bakery in Bridgeport, Connecticut. Yale students often bought pies at the nearby bakery. After eating the pies, they liked to toss the empty pie pans back and forth.

The metal frisbies, of course, were not safe. Anyone hit by the flying disk could get a bad lump or wound. So, in 1957, Walter Morrison and the Wham-O Manufacturing Company began making plastic models. The toy's name was changed to Frisbee, which is what it's still called today.

3. Who first had the idea of playing Frisbee?
   Ⓐ a baker in Bridgeport, Connecticut
   Ⓑ some students at Frisbie High School
   Ⓒ some students at Yale University
   Ⓓ Walter Morrison

4. Where were the first plastic Frisbees made?
   Ⓐ at Yale University
   Ⓑ at the Wham-O Manufacturing Company
   Ⓒ at the Frisbie Bakery
   Ⓓ at the Walter Morrison Manufacturing Company

Look at the answer choices for each question. Read why each answer choice is correct or not correct.

3. Who first had the idea of playing Frisbee?

Ⓐ a baker in Bridgeport, Connecticut

*This answer is not correct because the Bridgeport bakers made pies. The Yale students who bought the pies came up with the idea for the sport.*

Ⓑ some students at Frisbie High School

*This answer is not correct because Frisbie High School is never mentioned in the article.*

● some students at Yale University

*This answer is correct because the first sentence in the second paragraph states "Some students at Yale University invented this sport."*

Ⓓ Walter Morrison

*This answer is not correct because Walter Morrison made the first plastic Frisbees, but he did not invent the sport.*

4. Where were the first plastic Frisbees made?

Ⓐ at Yale University

*This answer is not correct because a sentence in the third paragraph states that Walter Morrison and the Wham-O Manufacturing Company began making the plastic models.*

● at the Wham-O Manufacturing Company

*This answer is correct because a sentence in the third paragraph states "Walter Morrison and the Wham-O Manufacturing Company began making plastic models."*

Ⓒ at the Frisbie Bakery

*This answer is not correct because the pie pans from the Frisbie Bakery were made of metal, not plastic.*

Ⓓ at the Walter Morrison Manufacturing Company

*This answer is not correct because the article does not mention a company with that name. Walter Morrison worked with the Wham-O Manufacturing Company to make the first plastic Frisbees.*

Writers use facts and details for many reasons.
When you read, look for sentences that

★ describe a person, place, or thing.

★ explain how to do something.

★ tell the order in which things happen.

★ share an experience, idea, or opinion.

**Read this article about ancient Rome. Then answer the questions.**

**A Powerful Empire**

Rome was once the center of a huge empire. The Roman Empire lasted hundreds of years. It ruled almost all of Europe, as well as parts of Africa and Asia. About 1,500 years ago, the Roman Empire fell apart.

Many Roman ideas still affect the way we live today. The Constitution of the United States is based on ideas in Roman laws. The alphabet we use is the Roman alphabet. Some of our months are named after Roman leaders. July is named after Julius Caesar. August is named in honor of Augustus Caesar, the first Roman emperor. Even the planets were named after Roman gods. Jupiter was the king of the gods. Mars was the god of war, and Venus was the goddess of love.

5. When did the Roman Empire end?
   Ⓐ about 150 years ago
   Ⓑ a hundred years ago
   Ⓒ about 1,500 years ago
   Ⓓ about 15,000 years ago

6. Which of these is a fact about the Roman Empire?
   Ⓐ All of our months are named after Roman leaders.
   Ⓑ Augustus Caesar was a Roman god.
   Ⓒ The first Roman emperor was Julius Caesar.
   Ⓓ It ruled almost all of Europe, as well as parts of Africa and Asia.

7. Whom were the planets named after?
   Ⓐ Roman cities
   Ⓑ Roman emperors
   Ⓒ Roman gods
   Ⓓ Roman months

8. Which detail tells more about the main idea of the first paragraph?
   Ⓐ The Constitution of the United States is based on ideas in Roman laws.
   Ⓑ The Roman Empire lasted hundreds of years.
   Ⓒ July is named after Julius Caesar.
   Ⓓ Many Roman ideas still affect the way we live today.

**Read this Greek myth. Then answer the questions.**

### Tell Me a Riddle

There once was a monster called the Sphinx. This beast had a woman's head, a lion's body, a serpent's tail, and an eagle's wings. The Sphinx lived on a mountaintop. Whenever travelers passed by, the creature asked them a riddle. Travelers who could not answer the riddle were eaten by the Sphinx. No one had ever escaped being killed.

One day, a Greek prince named Oedipus came by. The Sphinx challenged Oedipus to answer her riddle. Her riddle was: "What goes on four legs in the morning, two legs at noon, and three legs in the evening?"

Oedipus quickly solved the riddle. "A human," he replied. "For we humans crawl on all fours as babies. We walk on two legs as adults. Then we use a cane when we are old and weak."

The Sphinx could not believe that Oedipus had answered correctly. The creature was so ashamed that she flung herself over a cliff.

9. What is one detail that tells about the Sphinx?
   Ⓐ She was old and weak.
   Ⓑ She had three legs.
   Ⓒ She had a lion's body.
   Ⓓ She had an eagle's head.

10. A detail that tells about the main idea of paragraph two is
   Ⓐ Oedipus came by one day.
   Ⓑ the Sphinx had a serpent's tail.
   Ⓒ the Sphinx lived on a mountaintop.
   Ⓓ Oedipus was afraid of being eaten by the Sphinx.

11. Who was Oedipus?
   Ⓐ an ordinary traveler
   Ⓑ a Greek god
   Ⓒ a monster in the form of a human
   Ⓓ a Greek prince

12. Which of these tells more about the main idea of the last paragraph?
   Ⓐ The Sphinx was ashamed that Oedipus had solved the riddle.
   Ⓑ Oedipus took his time answering the riddle.
   Ⓒ Oedipus was afraid of the Sphinx.
   Ⓓ Travelers who could not answer the riddle were eaten by the Sphinx.

★ A test question about facts and details may ask you about something that is stated in a reading passage.

★ A test question about facts and details may ask you about the *who, what, where, when, why,* and *how* of the main idea.

**Here is an article about measurement. Read the article. Then do Numbers 13 and 14.**

### Measuring Tools

We use many different kinds of tools to measure things. Rulers, tape measures, and yardsticks measure length. Clocks, watches, and hourglasses measure time. Calendars measure time too, but in days and months, not minutes and hours.

Scales measure weight. Thermometers measure temperature. And protractors measure angles of common shapes.

A speedometer measures a vehicle's speed. An odometer measures the distance that the vehicle travels. For walkers, a pedometer can measure the number of steps they take.

Some people think that even intelligence can be measured. They use an IQ test. Still, tools can't be used to measure everything. For example, how would you measure happiness and friendship?

**Recalling Facts and Details**

13. An odometer is used to measure
    Ⓐ length.
    Ⓑ time.
    Ⓒ speed.
    Ⓓ distance.

**Recalling Facts and Details**

14. What tool measures weight?
    Ⓐ hourglass
    Ⓑ scale
    Ⓒ protractor
    Ⓓ pedometer

Here is a story about a girl who wants a pet. Read the story.
Then do Numbers 15 and 16.

**A Pet Platypus**

All of Lang's friends had pets. Samantha had a dog; Clare had a cat; and Theo had a parakeet. Lang wanted a pet too, but she wanted something unusual. She looked through some animal books for ideas. Finally, she saw an Australian mammal she liked. The animal was funny looking. It had a snout like a duck's bill, webbed feet, and a broad, flat tail. Lang had decided to get a platypus.

Lang begged her parents to get her a platypus pet for her birthday. Of course, her mom and dad had all kinds of objections.

"But Lang," they protested, "a platypus needs to swim in rivers and streams."

"It can swim in our bathtub," Lang replied.

"How will you feed it?" they added. "A platypus mostly eats insects and worms."

Lang answered, "Then the yard will get a good cleaning."

On the morning of Lang's birthday, her parents walked into her room. They were carrying a big wrapped box. Lang opened the gift and laughed. Inside the box was a life-size platypus. It was plastic, just right for swimming in the bathtub.

**Recalling Facts and Details**

15. What is one fact about a platypus?
   Ⓐ It has a duck's tail.
   Ⓑ It has webbed feet.
   Ⓒ It has a snout like a dog.
   Ⓓ It has feathers.

**Recalling Facts and Details**

16. Which of these is a fact from the story?
   Ⓐ A platypus can be purchased at a pet store.
   Ⓑ Lang wanted an unusual pet.
   Ⓒ Lang already had a pet dog.
   Ⓓ Lang's parents did not think a plastic platypus was a good idea.

# STRATEGY 3

## PART ONE: LEARN ABOUT SEQUENCE

**Read this story about how Tatiana prepared for a speech. As you read, think about the order in which things happened in the story.**

### Speak Up!
Tatiana was nervous about presenting a speech to her entire class. She made sure she was well prepared. On Monday, Tatiana chose a topic for her speech. On Tuesday, she gathered information about her topic. On Wednesday, she wrote the speech. She gave it an introduction, a body, and a conclusion. On Thursday, Tatiana copied her speech onto note cards. Finally, on Friday, she practiced her speech until she felt ready to present it.

The order in which things happened is

**On Monday, Tatiana chose a topic for her speech.**

**On Tuesday, she gathered information about her topic.**

**On Wednesday, she wrote the speech.**

**On Thursday, Tatiana copied her speech onto note cards.**

**Finally, on Friday, she practiced her speech until she felt ready to present it.**

The order in which things happen in a reading passage is called **sequence**. Sequence tells what happened first, second, third, and so on.

★ Clue words such as *first, next, then, last, finally, before,* and *after* often tell the order in which things happen.

★ Clues such as times of day, days of the week, months, and years tell when things happen.

★ Sometimes, there are no clue words. Thinking about the beginning, the middle, and the ending of a reading passage will help you understand the order in which things happen.

Read these directions to a number trick. As you read, think about what to do first, second, and so on. Then answer the questions.

**Math Magic**

Here is a fun number trick that's easy to solve. Just follow the directions carefully. First, think of a number. Second, double the number, and add two. Third, multiply the result by three. The next step is to add three. Then subtract your original number. After you do that, subtract four from the answer. Then subtract five. Finally, divide by five. Did you end up with the number with which you began?

1. What do you do first to solve the number trick?
   - Ⓐ Double the number.
   - Ⓑ Add three.
   - Ⓒ Subtract five.
   - Ⓓ Think of a number.

2. In the directions, which clue word tells what to do last?
   - Ⓐ then
   - Ⓑ third
   - Ⓒ finally
   - Ⓓ next

 Work with a partner. Talk about your answers to questions 1 and 2. Tell why you chose the answers you did.

**Remember: Sequence tells the order in which things happen.**

★ Look for clue words such as *first, next, then, last, finally, before,* and *after.*
These clue words often tell the order in which things happen.

★ Look for clues that tell about times of day, days of the week, months, or years.

★ When there are no clue words, think about the beginning, the middle, and the ending
of the reading passage. This will help you understand the order in which things happen.

**Read this story about a Jewish celebration. As you read, ask yourself,
"What happened first? What happened next? What happened after that?"
Then answer the questions.**

### Dreidel, Dreidel, Dreidel

Tonight is the first night of Hanukkah, the Jewish Festival of Lights. Ari and his cousins were looking forward to one of the holiday's special traditions. They were going to play a game of dreidel.

Ari gave each player an equal number of nuts to use as tokens. Then each player put one token in the center of the table. Rachel spun the four-sided top first. It landed with the Hebrew letter *hay* facing up. So she took half the tokens. Sonja went next. When she spun the dreidel, it landed with the letter *shin* faceup. Thus, she added one token to the pile. Daniel was the third player. On his turn, the spinning dreidel landed with *nun* showing. This meant that Daniel got nothing. Last, Ari took his turn. The dreidel landed with *gimel* faceup, and he won all the tokens. But the game didn't end. Each cousin put another token in the center of the table, and they continued to play.

hay

shin

nun

gimel

3. After Sonja took her turn,
   Ⓐ each player put a token in the center of the table.
   Ⓑ Daniel took his turn.
   Ⓒ Ari spun the dreidel.
   Ⓓ Rachel added a token to the pile.

4. Which clue word tells who went second?
   Ⓐ before
   Ⓑ then
   Ⓒ next
   Ⓓ last

**Look at the answer choices for each question. Read why each answer choice is correct or not correct.**

3. After Sonja took her turn,

Ⓐ each player put a token in the center of the table.

*This answer is not correct because each player put a token in the center of the table before any of the players took a turn.*

● Daniel took his turn.

*This answer is correct because the story states that Rachel spun the top first, Sonja went next, and Daniel was the third player. Thus, he had to be the player after Sonja.*

Ⓒ Ari spun the dreidel.

*This answer is not correct because the story states that Ari was the last of the four players and that Daniel was the third player. Ari couldn't go right after Sonja, because Daniel's turn was before his.*

Ⓓ Rachel added a token to the pile.

*This answer is not correct because the second paragraph states that Sonja, not Rachel, added a token to the pile.*

4. Which clue word tells who went second?

Ⓐ before

*This answer is not correct because this clue word is not used in the selection.*

Ⓑ then

*This answer is not correct because the word* then *is used in the second paragraph to tell what the players did after Ari gave them their tokens. No one had yet taken a turn.*

● next

*This answer is correct because this clue word tells who played after Rachel, the first player. The next player, Sonja, must then be the second player.*

Ⓓ last

*This answer is not correct because this clue word tells when Ari took his turn, and he was the fourth player.*

Many reading passages tell details and events in the order in which they happened. Look for sequence in these kinds of reading passages:

★ directions

★ journal entries

★ history articles

★ newspaper stories

★ stories, fables, and folktales

★ autobiographies and biographies

**Read this fable by Aesop. Then answer the questions.**

**The Fox and the Crow**

A crow was sitting on a branch of a tree. She held a piece of cheese in her beak. A fox caught sight of the crow and began thinking of a way to get the cheese. He went and stood under the tree and looked up. "What a noble bird I see above me!" he said. "Her beauty is without equal. The colors of her feathers are so pleasing. If only her voice is as sweet as her looks are fair. She ought, without doubt, to be queen of the birds."

Now, the crow was greatly flattered by this praise. Just to show the fox that she could sing, she gave a loud caw. Down came the cheese, of course.

The fox snatched up the cheese and said, "You have a lovely voice, madam, I see. But what you want is wits."

5. Which of these happened first?
   Ⓐ The fox stood under a tree.
   Ⓑ The fox began thinking of a way to get the crow's cheese.
   Ⓒ A fox saw a crow in a tree.
   Ⓓ The fox praised the crow's beauty.

6. Right after the crow gave a loud caw,
   Ⓐ the cheese came down.
   Ⓑ the fox praised the crow's voice.
   Ⓒ the fox snatched up the cheese.
   Ⓓ the fox told the crow she needed wits.

7. Which clue word tells what the fox did last?
   Ⓐ after
   Ⓑ last
   Ⓒ finally
   Ⓓ There is no clue word.

8. What did the fox do before snatching up the cheese?
   Ⓐ He sang a sweet song.
   Ⓑ He said the crow ought to be queen of the birds.
   Ⓒ He climbed the tree.
   Ⓓ He scolded the crow.

**Read this autobiography of a folk heroine. Then answer the questions.**

### The Life and Adventures of Calamity Jane

My maiden name was Martha Jane Canary. I was born in Princeton, Missouri, on May 1, 1852. As a child, I always had a fondness for adventure and outdoor exercise. I began to ride horses at an early age. In time, I became an expert rider.

In 1865, our family moved to Virginia City, Montana. It took us five months to make the journey. On the way, I spent most of my time hunting with the men. I was considered a remarkably good shot for a girl of my age.

Mother died in 1866, and I left Montana for Utah. I remained in Utah until 1867, when my father died. In 1870, I joined General Custer as a scout in Wyoming. When I joined Custer, I donned the uniform of a soldier. I soon got to be perfectly at home in men's clothes.

As a scout, I performed a great many dangerous missions. In 1873, we were ordered to crush an Indian revolt. Our commander, Captain Egan, was shot. I galloped to his side in time to catch him as he was falling from his saddle. I lifted him onto my horse and succeeded in getting him safely to the fort. On recovering, Captain Egan said, "I name you Calamity Jane, the heroine of the plains." I have borne that name up to the present time.

9. In the autobiography, clues that tell about the sequence are
   Ⓐ months.
   Ⓑ days of the week.
   Ⓒ times of day.
   Ⓓ years.

10. What happened in Calamity Jane's life during the year 1867?
   Ⓐ Her mother died.
   Ⓑ Her father died.
   Ⓒ She became a scout.
   Ⓓ She earned her nickname.

11. When did Calamity Jane go to Wyoming?
   Ⓐ 1852
   Ⓑ 1865
   Ⓒ 1870
   Ⓓ 1873

12. What happened just after Captain Egan was shot?
   Ⓐ He nicknamed the woman who saved him.
   Ⓑ He arrived at the fort.
   Ⓒ Calamity Jane galloped to his side.
   Ⓓ Calamity Jane lifted him onto her horse.

★ A test question about sequence may ask you when certain things happened in a reading passage.

★ A test question about sequence may ask you to put events from a reading passage in order.

★ A test question about sequence may contain words such as *first, second, last, before,* or *after.*

**Here are directions for making a flip book. Read the directions. Then do Numbers 13 and 14.**

Have you ever wondered how cartoons are made? Special artists called animators create cartoons. To make a short cartoon, they must draw thousands of pictures. In each picture, the characters are drawn in a slightly different position. When the drawings pass very quickly before the viewers' eyes, the characters seem to move.

You can see how this works by making a flip book. To begin, cut a sheet of stiff paper into 25 or 30 small rectangles, all the same size.

Next, choose a simple movement to draw, such as running, kicking, or jumping. Ask a friend to model the movement for you. Have your friend hold different poses while you draw a quick sketch on each rectangle. Keep the drawings simple by using stick figures to show the movement. Also, make sure that you draw each sketch in the same spot on each page. Leave space on the left-hand side to staple the pictures together, and number the back of each drawing.

When you are done, arrange the pictures in the correct order and staple them together. Then hold the book in your left hand. Flip the pages of the book with your right hand as fast as you can. As you do this, your figure will appear to move.

## Understanding Sequence

13. Which step is done second to make a flip book?

    Ⓐ Draw stick figures.

    Ⓑ Ask a friend to model poses.

    Ⓒ Cut paper into rectangles.

    Ⓓ Choose a simple movement to draw.

## Understanding Sequence

14. The boxes tell about some of the steps in making a flip book.

|  | Number the back of each drawing. | Arrange the pictures in order. |
|---|---|---|
| 1 | 2 | 3 |

Which of these belongs in box 1?

    Ⓐ Flip the pages quickly.

    Ⓑ Draw simple sketches.

    Ⓒ Hold the book in one hand.

    Ⓓ Staple the pictures together.

Here is an article about getting dressed. Read the article.
Then do Numbers 15 and 16.

From 1100 to 1300, great castles were built all over Europe. Kings and powerful lords built the castles to defend their lands from enemies. Hundreds of knights lived in the castles. They fought for the kings and lords. A knight had to be well trained and always ready for battle. A knight also had to dress well for his job. His life depended on the heavy suit of armor he wore.

A knight couldn't dress himself. A squire had to help him. A squire was a boy who was training to be a knight. First, the knight dressed in a loose shirt and long leg coverings. Second, he put a padded tunic over his shirt and a padded cap on his head. Over the padded tunic, the knight put on a chain-mail shirt. Chain mail is made of small iron rings linked together. The knight then added a chain-mail hood and leggings.

Next, the squire strapped metal guards onto the knight's chest, legs, arms, and shoulders. The squire then pulled a cloth tunic over the knight's armor. This tunic kept the metal armor from rusting in the rain. The tunic bore a special design, called a coat of arms, to show who the knight was.

After the tunic was on, the squire covered the knight's head and face with a metal helmet. The squire also pulled metal gloves over the knight's hands and placed spurs at his heels. Last, the squire handed the knight his sword, lance, and shield. Finally, the knight was ready to climb on his horse and ride off to battle.

## Understanding Sequence

15. What did a knight put on before his chain mail?
   Ⓐ a metal chest guard
   Ⓑ a padded tunic
   Ⓒ a tunic with a coat of arms
   Ⓓ metal gloves

## Understanding Sequence

16. After the cloth tunic was pulled over the knight's armor, the squire added
   Ⓐ metal leg and arm guards.
   Ⓑ a padded cap.
   Ⓒ a metal helmet.
   Ⓓ spurs.

## PART ONE: READ A LETTER

Here is a letter written by Elizabeth Blackwell. Read the letter.
Then do Numbers 1 through 6.

June 24, 1863

Dear Emily,

Thank you for your lovely letter. I'm flattered that you'd like to follow in my footsteps. Here are the answers to the questions you asked me.

I was born in England in 1821. My family moved to the United States when I was 11. My father died six years later, and I had to go to work. So, I became a teacher. Teaching was one of the few jobs a woman could have at that time.

I decided to become a doctor in 1844, after visiting a dying friend. She told me that I was clever and should consider studying medicine. I reminded her that there were no women doctors in the United States. She replied that she might not be dying if a woman doctor had treated her.

I continued teaching to earn the money for medical school. The principal of my school was a kind doctor named Samuel Dickson. He encouraged me and gave me his medical books to study.

When I applied to medical schools, 28 schools turned me down. I had almost given up hope. But, at last, the Geneva Medical College, in New York, said yes.

Being the only woman in a class of 150 men was difficult. When I graduated in 1849, though, I was first in my class. I was also the first woman in the United States to receive a medical degree.

I have one main purpose as a doctor. I want to teach women how to care for themselves and their children. I opened a clinic for them. It now includes a medical college for women. Maybe you'd like to apply there someday.

I wish you all the best.

Sincerely,
Elizabeth Blackwell

## Finding Main Idea

1. What is this letter mostly about?
   - Ⓐ the life of Elizabeth Blackwell
   - Ⓑ women's job choices in the 1800s
   - Ⓒ an early death of a good friend
   - Ⓓ getting into medical school

## Recalling Facts and Details

4. Who first inspired Elizabeth Blackwell to become a doctor?
   - Ⓐ her father
   - Ⓑ a dying friend
   - Ⓒ Samuel Dickson
   - Ⓓ the teachers at Geneva Medical College

## Finding Main Idea

2. What would be a good title for this selection?
   - Ⓐ "Surviving Medical School"
   - Ⓑ "The First Woman Doctor"
   - Ⓒ "A Teacher's Life"
   - Ⓓ "Making a Promise"

## Understanding Sequence

5. Which of these happened first?
   - Ⓐ Blackwell got turned down by 28 medical schools.
   - Ⓑ Blackwell taught to earn money for medical school.
   - Ⓒ Blackwell opened a women's clinic.
   - Ⓓ Blackwell entered Geneva Medical College.

## Recalling Facts and Details

3. Elizabeth Blackwell came to the United States at the age of
   - Ⓐ 6.
   - Ⓑ 24.
   - Ⓒ 29.
   - Ⓓ 11.

## Understanding Sequence

6. You can tell the sequence in the letter mostly by
   - Ⓐ looking for clues that tell about times of day, days of the week, months, or years.
   - Ⓑ thinking about the main idea.
   - Ⓒ finding facts and details.
   - Ⓓ thinking about the beginning, the middle, and the ending.

Here is a story from Syria. Read the story. Then do Numbers 7 through 12.

Once there was a rich businessman who bought ten donkeys to lend out for hire. The first day, he hired out his donkeys to a wood gatherer. At night, the wood gatherer returned the donkeys and paid the businessman his money.

On the road to his tent, it occurred to the man to count the donkeys. He found there were only nine, for he did not count the one on which he was sitting.

"The wood gatherer stole one of my animals," he cried.

He got off the donkey in a rage and counted all over again. Now there were ten.

"The wood gatherer did not cheat me after all," he thought.

He rode on, and it occurred to him to count the animals again. He did, and there were only nine. Once more, he did not have the understanding to count the one on which he was sitting.

"That thieving wood gatherer took one of my donkeys."

The angry man leapt out of his saddle and counted the animals all over again. And again there were ten.

"I accused the wood gatherer wrongfully. All the animals are here."

So the man got on his donkey and rode on. But he had no peace. He could not understand why there should be a different number of donkeys each time he counted them.

"Whenever I mount my donkey, I lose one. When I get off, the beast comes back. I think I'd better stay off altogether, because next time I mount my donkey, I may lose one for certain."

So the man walked the long distance to his home on foot.

## Finding Main Idea

7. The main idea of the story is found
   Ⓐ in the first paragraph.
   Ⓑ in the middle of the story.
   Ⓒ in the last paragraph.
   Ⓓ by thinking about the most important idea in the story.

## Recalling Facts and Details

10. Which detail tells that the man was angry?
    Ⓐ He got off his donkey in a rage.
    Ⓑ He did not count the donkey on which he was sitting.
    Ⓒ He couldn't understand why his count was different each time.
    Ⓓ He rode on toward his tent.

## Finding Main Idea

8. A good title for this story is
   Ⓐ "Ten Counting Donkeys."
   Ⓑ "A Rich Man Poor in Understanding."
   Ⓒ "A Clever Thief."
   Ⓓ "The Long Journey Home."

## Understanding Sequence

11. Which of these happened last?
    Ⓐ The man leapt out of his saddle.
    Ⓑ The standing man counted ten donkeys.
    Ⓒ The man thought he should stay off his donkey altogether.
    Ⓓ The man was sorry that he called the wood gatherer a thief.

## Recalling Facts and Details

9. Who hired the man's donkeys?
   Ⓐ a thief
   Ⓑ a woodcutter
   Ⓒ a wood gatherer
   Ⓓ a businessman

## Understanding Sequence

12. The boxes tell some things that happened in the story.

| The man hired out ten donkeys. | | The man counted nine donkeys. |
|---|---|---|
| 1 | 2 | 3 |

Which of these belongs in box 2?
Ⓐ The man counted ten donkeys.
Ⓑ The man got off his donkey.
Ⓒ The donkeys were returned.
Ⓓ The man thought that a donkey had been stolen.

## PART ONE: LEARN ABOUT CAUSE AND EFFECT

**Read this article about birds that don't fly. As you read, think about one thing that happened to some birds and why.**

All birds have wings, but not all birds fly. Scientists believe that, at one time, all birds could fly. In time, however, some birds no longer needed to fly to survive. So, these birds became flightless. The two most common flightless birds are penguins and ostriches.

Penguins have flippers instead of wings. They use these flippers to help them swim underwater at fast speeds. Ostriches also move quickly, even though they are the largest living birds. Their wings help them balance as they run. These birds can run at speeds up to 35 miles per hour.

One thing that happened to some birds and why is

What happened: **They became flightless.**
Why it happened: **They no longer needed to fly to survive.**

What happens and why is called **cause and effect.**
*Why* something happens is the **cause.** *They no longer needed to fly to survive.*
*What* happens because of the cause is the **effect.** *They became flightless.*

★ A cause is the reason that something happens.

★ An effect is what happens as a result of the cause.

★ Clue words such as *so, so that, since, because,* and *if* often signal cause and effect. Other clues words are *reason* and *as a result.*

**Read this journal entry written by a girl named Hannah. As you read, look for clue words to help you understand what happens and why it happens. Then answer the questions.**

January 15

Today, my parents took me to an art museum. The museum was exhibiting the paintings of Vincent van Gogh, a Dutch painter of the late 1800s. Because I like to paint, my parents thought I would enjoy seeing van Gogh's work. I just thought I'd be bored.

Boy, was I ever surprised! The minute I walked into the van Gogh gallery, I was fascinated. Van Gogh used bold, bright colors to express his feelings about what he saw. I spent hours looking at van Gogh's vivid paintings. When it was finally time to leave, I was disappointed. My parents had to drag me away, because I was having such a good time.

1. Hannah's parents thought she would enjoy seeing van Gogh's work because she
   Ⓐ likes art museums.
   Ⓑ has always enjoyed van Gogh's work.
   Ⓒ likes to paint.
   Ⓓ had nothing else to do.

2. Which clue word or words signals the reason that Hannah's parents had to drag her away?
   Ⓐ so that
   Ⓑ because
   Ⓒ since
   Ⓓ if

 Work with a partner. Talk about your answers to questions 1 and 2. Tell why you chose the answers you did.

**Remember: What happens and why is called cause and effect.**

★ To find a cause, look for a reason that something happened.
Ask yourself, "*Why* did it happen?"

★ To find an effect, look for a result, or something that happened.
Ask yourself, "*What* happened?"

★ Look for clue words that signal cause and effect, such as *so, so that, since, because, if, reason,* and *as a result.*

**Read this silly rhyme about a young lady. As you read, ask yourself,
"*What* are some things that happen in the rhyme? *Why* do these things happen?"
Then answer the questions.**

### There Was a Young Lady Residing at Prague

There was a young lady residing at Prague
Whose ideas were really most wonderfully vague.
When anyone said to her: "What a fine day!"
"Roast chicken is nice," she would dreamily say,
"And a mushroom on toast is the very best thing
To make a canary or hummingbird sing."
The people of Prague thought this conduct so strange,
They quickly decided she needed a change,
So they packed her with care in a box with some hay,
And paid her expenses as far as Bombay.

3. Why did everyone think that the lady's conduct was strange?
   Ⓐ She made odd remarks.
   Ⓑ She ate a mushroom on toast.
   Ⓒ She made a canary sing.
   Ⓓ She had unusual dreams.

4. Because the people of Prague decided that the lady needed a change, they
   Ⓐ told her to have a fine day.
   Ⓑ woke her from her dreams.
   Ⓒ paid her expenses for a doctor's care.
   Ⓓ packed her in a box and sent her to Bombay.

Look at the answer choices for each question. Read why each answer choice is correct or not correct.

3. Why did everyone think that the lady's conduct was strange?

● She made odd remarks.

*This answer is correct because whenever anyone said to her "What a fine day!", the young lady would say something odd, such as "Roast chicken is nice."*

Ⓑ She ate a mushroom on toast.

*This answer is not correct because the lady said that "And a mushroom on toast is the very best thing/To make a canary or hummingbird sing." She does not say that she herself eats a mushroom on toast. Also, this would not be reason enough to think that someone's conduct is strange.*

Ⓒ She made a canary sing.

*This answer is not correct because the lady did not say that she could make a canary sing. She said that a mushroom on toast was the very best thing to make a canary sing.*

Ⓓ She had unusual dreams.

*This answer is not correct because nothing is said about the lady's dreams. The rhyme says that the lady spoke dreamily, but this does not refer to her dreams.*

4. Because the people of Prague decided that the lady needed a change, they

Ⓐ told her to have a fine day.

*This answer is not correct because the people told the young lady to have a fine day before they decided she needed a change. It was her response to their comment that they thought was strange.*

Ⓑ woke her from her dreams.

*This answer is not correct because the rhyme never says that the young lady was dreaming or that she was awakened from her dreams.*

Ⓒ paid her expenses for a doctor's care.

*This answer is not correct because no doctor is mentioned in the rhyme.*

● packed her in a box and sent her to Bombay.

*This answer is correct because the effect is stated directly in the rhyme, after the cause. The clue word so signals the cause-and-effect relationship.*

Sometimes, there are no clue words to signal cause and effect in a reading passage. When there are no clue words, do the following:

★ To find an effect, think about *what* happened.

★ To find a cause, think about *how* or *why* it happened.

★ Think about what you already know about how one thing might cause another thing to happen.

**Read this article about a spring holiday. Then answer the questions.**

**April Fool!**

On April 1, people like to play jokes on one another. This day is called April Fools' Day. No one is sure how the custom to fool people on April 1 began. Some people think the tradition began in France. Until the mid-1500s, April 1 had been the first day of the new year. Then, in 1564, the calendar was changed. The first day of the new year was moved to January 1. Some people, though, still celebrated New Year's Day on April 1. Others made fun of them for celebrating the new year on the wrong day. They called these people "April fools."

When the new year began on April 1, people gave gifts to one another. After the new calendar changed New Year's Day to January 1, some people still gave presents on April 1. But they chose joke gifts. As a result, people also came to play jokes on one another on April Fools' Day.

5. How did people come to play jokes on one another on April Fools' Day?
   Ⓐ They were not allowed to give gifts on this day.
   Ⓑ They once gave joke gifts to one another on this day.
   Ⓒ It was a French custom to play jokes on this day.
   Ⓓ They wanted to act like fools.

6. Which clue word or phrase signals the reason that people play jokes on April 1?
   Ⓐ since
   Ⓑ so
   Ⓒ as a result
   Ⓓ because

7. When the calendar was changed in 1564,
   Ⓐ January 1 became New Year's Day.
   Ⓑ April 1 became New Year's Day.
   Ⓒ the month of January was dropped from the calendar.
   Ⓓ people began acting like fools.

8. Why were people called "April fools"?
   Ⓐ Before 1564, they celebrated the new year on April 1.
   Ⓑ They liked to give joke gifts in April.
   Ⓒ They thought that April 1 still began the new year.
   Ⓓ After 1564, they continued to celebrate April 1 as New Year's Day.

**Read this brochure for a unique tourist attraction. Then answer the questions.**

$\mathcal{L}$ooking for things to do in San Jose, California? Why not visit the city's largest house? The Winchester House is fun to visit because of its unusual history and uncommon style.

$\mathcal{T}$he Winchester House was once an eight-room farmhouse. It was built by Oliver Winchester, the inventor of the Winchester rifle. Oliver died in 1886. His widow, Sarah, felt great sorrow. She went to see a woman who claimed she could speak with the dead. She told Sarah that spirits of people killed by her husband's rifles were angry. The spirits were a danger to Sarah. There was only one way for Sarah to avoid danger. She must keep adding on to her house.

$\mathcal{O}$ver the next 36 years, the Winchester House grew and changed. Carpenters worked 24 hours a day. To keep them busy, Sarah often ordered them to build useless features. Many doors opened to blank walls. Some staircases led nowhere.

$\mathcal{B}$uilding didn't stop on the Winchester House until Sarah's death, in 1922. By then, the house had become a mansion seven stories high, with 160 rooms.

9. What happened as a result of Sarah's visit to the woman?
   - Ⓐ Sarah talked to her dead husband.
   - Ⓑ Sarah began adding on to her house.
   - Ⓒ Sarah ignored the woman's advice.
   - Ⓓ Winchester rifles were no longer made.

10. Why did Sarah add useless features to her house?
   - Ⓐ to keep the carpenters busy
   - Ⓑ to trick the spirits of the dead
   - Ⓒ to make the house more mysterious
   - Ⓓ to please tourists

11. Construction on the Winchester House stopped because
   - Ⓐ the carpenters had finished the job.
   - Ⓑ Sarah could no longer afford to keep adding on.
   - Ⓒ the house had become a popular tourist attraction.
   - Ⓓ Sarah died.

12. One reason the Winchester House is a fun place to visit is that
   - Ⓐ it is haunted.
   - Ⓑ it is unusually small.
   - Ⓒ it has an unusual history.
   - Ⓓ it is the largest house in California.

★ A test question about cause and effect may ask you *what* happened in a reading passage (the effect).

★ A test question about cause and effect may ask you *why* something happened (the cause).

★ A test question about cause and effect often contains words such as *because, why, reason,* or *what happened.*

**Here is a story from Mexico. Read the story. Then do Numbers 13 and 14.**

### Twelve on a Bench

One day, the people of Lagos got into a great argument. Finally, they asked the oldest and wisest men of Lagos for their help. The twelve men decided to meet on the bench in the town square to discuss the matter.

Six of the men arrived first. Each man wore a big, wide sombrero. It was a hot day, so the six men took off their straw hats. As they sat down, they put the hats right next to them. The hats took up more space than the men did, so the bench was full.

Soon, the other six men came. They tried to sit down, but there wasn't any space.

"There is no room on the bench for us," said one of the men standing.

"I think the bench has shrunk," answered one of those sitting.

"Why don't we try and stretch the bench?" suggested the oldest man.

So, the six sitting on the bench arose, put their sombreros on their heads, and got hold of one end of the bench. Then the six standing got hold of the other end of the bench, and each group began pulling the wood as hard as they could. After some time, they put the bench down.

All twelve men sat down, each with his sombrero on his head. Of course, now the hats took up no space, and there was plenty of room for all.

"Now that we have done a fine job stretching that bench, we can discuss our problem," spoke the oldest. So the men of Lagos, feeling very pleased with themselves, went on to their discussion.

**Recognizing Cause and Effect**

13. Why did the first six men take off their hats?
   Ⓐ They were being polite.
   Ⓑ The straw hats were itchy.
   Ⓒ It was a hot day for wearing a hat.
   Ⓓ The bench had room for the hats.

**Recognizing Cause and Effect**

14. What happened to the bench as a result of being pulled?
   Ⓐ The bench became longer.
   Ⓑ Nothing, but the men thought the bench was longer.
   Ⓒ The bench became shorter.
   Ⓓ The bench broke in half.

Here is an article about the human body. Read the article.
Then do Numbers 15 and 16.

### The Wonders of the Human Body

How the human body works is a mystery to most people. For example, do you know why you blink? Or blush? Or sneeze? For every bodily mystery, there is a scientific answer.

Everyone blinks—thousands of times a day. Blinking is important because it washes tears over the eyeballs. These tears clean away dirt and dust. If you stopped blinking, the outer covering of your eyeballs would dry out and get infected. You might even go blind.

Blushing can be embarrassing, but there's nothing you can do to stop it. People usually blush when someone teases or threatens them. One part of the brain sends a message to another part. The body is told to get ready to defend itself. Extra blood flows to the muscles. When blood rushes to your arms and legs, no one notices it. But there's no hiding the redness in your face!

Sneezing is the way your body protects your lungs. If dust sneaks past your nose to the throat, the brain sends out an alarm. This warning causes the tubes in the throat to tighten so that the dust can't get through to the lungs. But when you try to breathe, pressure builds up in the narrow tubes. When the pressure becomes too great, the tubes are forced open with a quick blast of air. Achooo!

## Recognizing Cause and Effect

15. Blinking is important because it
   Ⓐ prevents pressure from building up behind the eyes.
   Ⓑ tells the body to get ready to defend itself.
   Ⓒ helps the body protect the lungs.
   Ⓓ cleans away dirt and dust from the eyes.

## Recognizing Cause and Effect

16. What usually happens when people are teased or threatened?
   Ⓐ They blink.
   Ⓑ They blush.
   Ⓒ They sneeze.
   Ⓓ They hiccup.

## PART ONE: LEARN ABOUT COMPARING AND CONTRASTING

Read this short history of blue jeans. As you read, think about the ways the first jeans and modern jeans are alike and the ways they are different.

> During the California Gold Rush of 1849, miners discovered that digging for gold wore out their pants quickly. A young immigrant named Levi Strauss sold the miners a strong blue cotton cloth called denim. They had the denim cloth made into work pants. Before long, all the gold miners were wearing these tough but comfortable jeans.
>
> Modern jeans are still made of blue denim. However, they come in many other colors and styles too. Also, these popular pants are no longer just work clothes. Today, people still wear jeans for work. But they also wear them for school, for play, or just for looking good.

Ways in which the first jeans and modern jeans are alike:

**Both are made of denim.**
**Both are worn for work.**

Ways in which the first jeans and modern jeans are different:

**The first jeans came in one color and style, but modern jeans come in many colors and styles.**

**The first jeans were just work clothes, but modern jeans are also worn for school, for play, and for looking good.**

Finding how two or more things are alike and how they are different is called **comparing and contrasting**. Comparing is finding how things are alike. Contrasting is finding how things are different.

★ Clue words that signal how things are alike are *both, same, like, alike,* and *similar.*

★ Clue words that signal how things are different are *but, unlike, different, however,* and *whereas.*

★ People, places, objects, and events can all be compared and contrasted.

**Read this article about baseball in Japan. As you read, look for clue words that tell how Japanese baseball is like American baseball and how it is different. Then answer the questions.**

### Play Ball!

People say that baseball is "as American as apple pie." The people of Japan may not agree. They love the sport too. Millions of Japanese fans also attend baseball games or watch them on TV.

Like the United States, Japan has two major leagues. Every fall, the best team from each league competes in the Japan Series. The Japan Series is similar to our World Series.

There are also differences between Japanese baseball and American baseball. Baseball fields in Japan are smaller than those in the United States. In Japan, each major league has only six teams. The major leagues in the United States have about 15 teams each. Japanese teams also play fewer games each season than American teams.

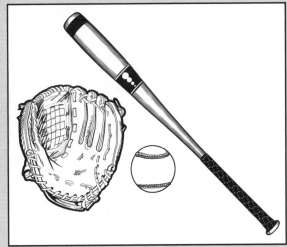

1. How are baseball teams in Japan and in the United States alike?

    (A) Both compete in the Japan Series.

    (B) Both have two major leagues.

    (C) Both play the same number of games each season.

    (D) Both play on small fields.

2. Which clue word signals that the Japan Series and the World Series are alike?

    (A) different

    (B) same

    (C) similar

    (D) like

Work with a partner. Talk about your answers to questions 1 and 2. Tell why you chose the answers you did.

**Remember:** Comparing is finding ways that things are alike.
Contrasting is finding ways that things are different.

★ Look for clue words that signal a likeness, or comparison, such as *both*, *same*, *like*, *alike*, and *similar*.

★ Look for clue words that signal a difference, or contrast, such as *but*, *unlike*, *different*, *however*, and *whereas*.

★ Look for people, places, objects, and events that are being compared and contrasted.

**Read this article about crocodiles and alligators. As you read, ask yourself, "How are these animals alike? How are they different?" Then answer the questions.**

### Reptile Relatives

Most people can't tell the difference between an alligator and a crocodile. That's not surprising. These large reptiles look a lot alike. Both have four short legs and a long, powerful tail. Their skin is greenish brown and covered with scales. Also, their eyes and nostrils are on top of their head.

There are many ways to tell the two reptiles apart. An alligator has a broader head and a rounder snout. A crocodile has a narrow head and a long, pointed snout. When an alligator's jaws are closed, its lower teeth are hidden. But when a crocodile's jaws are shut, a tooth sticks out on each side.

Both reptiles must live in warm waters to survive. Alligators like only fresh water. Crocodiles, however, sometimes swim out to sea for a short time. Alligators are found in only two places. They live in parts of China and in the southeastern United States. Crocodiles, however, live in many places. They are found in South America, Central America, Africa, Asia, and Australia. A few are also found in southern Florida, with their alligator cousins.

3. In what way are alligators and crocodiles alike?
   Ⓐ Their lower teeth don't show when their jaws are shut.
   Ⓑ They both have narrow heads.
   Ⓒ Their eyes and nostrils are on top of their head.
   Ⓓ They both live only in fresh water.

4. Which clue word signals how the places in which crocodiles live are different from the places in which alligators live?
   Ⓐ both
   Ⓑ but
   Ⓒ different
   Ⓓ however

**Look at the answer choices for each question. Read why each answer choice is correct or not correct.**

3. In what way are alligators and crocodiles alike?

   Ⓐ Their lower teeth don't show when their jaws are shut.

   *This answer is not correct because an alligator's lower teeth are hidden when its jaws are closed. When a crocodile's jaws are shut, a tooth on each side sticks out.*

   Ⓑ They both have narrow heads.

   *This answer is not correct because crocodiles have a narrow head. Alligators have a shorter, broader head.*

   ● Their eyes and nostrils are on top of their head.

   *This answer is correct because this is a comparison that is stated in the first paragraph.*

   Ⓓ They both live only in fresh water.

   *This answer is not correct because alligators live only in fresh water. Crocodiles can also live in the sea for a short time. Both reptiles, however, must live in warm waters to survive.*

4. Which clue word signals how the places in which crocodiles live are different from the places in which alligators live?

   Ⓐ both

   *This answer is not correct because the word* both *is usually used to compare things, not contrast them. In the last paragraph, the word* both *is used to explain that the environment in which these reptiles live is the same: "Both reptiles must live in warm waters to survive."*

   Ⓑ but

   *This answer is not correct because the word* but *is not used in the paragraph that describes the places where the reptiles live.*

   Ⓒ different

   *This answer is not correct because the word* different *is not used in the article.*

   ● however

   *This answer is correct because a contrast between where crocodiles and alligators live is in the last paragraph. The paragraph states "Alligators are found in only two places. . . . Crocodiles, however, live in many places. They are found in South America, Central America, Africa, Asia, and Australia."*

Sometimes, there are no clue words in a reading passage to signal that things are being compared or contrasted. When there are no clue words,

★ think about the people, places, objects, or events that you read about. Ask yourself, "How are they alike? How are they different?"

★ think about the people, places, objects, or events that you read about. Ask yourself, "What things are compared or contrasted? In what ways are they compared? In what ways are they contrasted?"

**Read this article written by Adina. Then answer the questions.**

### Best Friends

My best friend, Rajini, and I have a lot in common. We were both born on June 24 in India. I was born in the old city of Delhi. Rajini was born in New Delhi, the capital. Our families moved to the United States when Rajini and I were two years old.

Rajini and I are in the fourth grade at the Estabrook School. She has Mr. Saxon. I have Ms. Ortega. After school, we take dance lessons together, and we have the same piano teacher. I study classical piano. Rajini studies jazz.

At home, I have two older brothers. Rajini has a younger sister. Our fathers are both engineers. My mother is an architect, whereas Rajini's mother is a writer. Our families live in the same apartment building. We're not allowed to have dogs or cats in our building. Rajini, though, does have a goldfish.

Some people think that Rajini and I are sisters. We're both tall and thin and have short black hair. Only I, however, wear glasses. If I take them off, it's hard to tell us apart.

5. How is Rajini like Adina?
   Ⓐ She was also born in Delhi, India.
   Ⓑ Her birthday is also June 24.
   Ⓒ She also likes jazz.
   Ⓓ She also wears glasses.

6. In what way are the girls different?
   Ⓐ Adina has two older brothers, and Rajini has an older sister.
   Ⓑ Adina's mother is an architect, and Rajini's mother is an engineer.
   Ⓒ Adina does not have a pet, but Rajini does.
   Ⓓ Adina lives in the city, but Rajini lives in a small town.

7. Which of these tells one thing the girls have in common?
   Ⓐ Both are in fourth grade.
   Ⓑ Both attend Brook School.
   Ⓒ Both have the same classroom teacher.
   Ⓓ Both study classical piano.

8. Adina compared her looks to Rajini's by saying that
   Ⓐ no one can ever tell them apart.
   Ⓑ both of them are short and thin.
   Ⓒ both of them have brown hair.
   Ⓓ people think that they are sisters.

Read this chart, which describes some of the ways frogs and toads are alike and different. Then answer the questions.

| Quality | Frogs | Toads |
|---|---|---|
| Can survive only in moist conditions | √ | √ |
| Live mostly in water | √ | |
| Live mostly on land | | √ |
| Are cold-blooded animals | √ | √ |
| Lay their eggs in the water | √ | √ |
| Begin life as tadpoles with gills and tails | √ | √ |
| Adults have lungs instead of gills | √ | √ |
| Adults have no tail | √ | √ |
| Use long, sticky tongue to catch insects | √ | √ |
| Feed mostly on insects | √ | √ |
| Have moist, smooth skin | √ | |
| Have dry, bumpy skin | | √ |
| Have long, powerful back legs for leaping | √ | |
| Have shorter legs | | √ |
| Are excellent jumpers | √ | |
| Do more hopping than jumping | | √ |
| Color usually matches their surroundings | √ | √ |

9. Which of these tells one way frogs and toads are different?
   (A) Only frogs lay their eggs in the water.
   (B) Toads' color matches their surroundings.
   (C) Only frogs do more hopping than jumping.
   (D) Toads live mostly on land.

10. One way that frogs and toads are alike is that
    (A) they have long, powerful back legs.
    (B) they use their tongues to catch insects.
    (C) they have moist skin.
    (D) they live mostly in water.

11. What three qualities do frogs have in common with toads?
    (A) are cold-blooded, have bumpy skin, color matches their surroundings
    (B) lay their eggs in the water, are excellent jumpers, live mostly in water
    (C) adults have lungs, eat insects, can survive only in moist conditions
    (D) begin life as tadpoles, adults have no tail, have dry skin

12. Which of these is true?
    (A) Frogs and toads are alike in more ways than they are different.
    (B) Frogs and toads are different in more ways than they are alike.
    (C) Toads can do everything that frogs can do and more.
    (D) Frogs are just like toads, except that frogs lay their eggs in the water.

★ A test question about comparing and contrasting may ask you how things are alike or how they are different.

★ A test question about comparing and contrasting usually contains a clue word. Words such as *same, like, alike,* and *similar* signal that you are to compare things. Words such as *different, unlike,* or *not like* signal that you are to contrast things.

**Here is an article about something that seems unlikely, but is true. Read the article. Then do Numbers 13 and 14.**

### Unlikely Likenesses

In 1860, Abraham Lincoln became president of the United States. The secretary who helped him with his work was a man. His last name was Kennedy. One Friday, in 1865, the president and his wife went to a play at Ford's Theater in Washington, D.C. During the play, John Wilkes Booth shot the president in the back of the head. Booth then ran to a warehouse to hide. Lincoln died the next morning. Andrew Johnson, his vice president, became the new president. Johnson was born in 1808.

In 1960, John F. Kennedy was elected president. His secretary was Evelyn Lincoln. One Friday, in 1963, the president and his wife were riding through Dallas, Texas. Suddenly, bullets struck the back of the president's head. A man named Lee Harvey Oswald fired the shots from a warehouse. He ran to a theater to hide. Kennedy died within the hour. His vice president, Lyndon Johnson, took over as president. Johnson was born in 1908.

**Comparing and Contrasting**

13. What is similar about the lives of John F. Kennedy and Abraham Lincoln?

Ⓐ Both men had a vice president named Johnson take over.

Ⓑ Both men died on a Friday.

Ⓒ Both men were born in a year ending with the numbers 08.

Ⓓ Both men had secretaries named Lincoln.

**Comparing and Contrasting**

14. The stories of John Wilkes Booth and Lee Harvey Oswald are different because

Ⓐ Booth shot a president on a Friday, but Oswald did not.

Ⓑ Booth ran to a warehouse, but Oswald did not.

Ⓒ Oswald shot a president from behind, but Booth did not.

Ⓓ Oswald did not intend to shoot the president, but Booth did.

Here is a friendly letter about family vacation plans. Read the letter. Then do Numbers 15 and 16.

623 Oakdale Drive
Lancaster, PA 17603
May 15, 2000

Dear Greg,

Our family is trying to decide where we will spend our vacation this year. My dad wants to go camping. My mom wants to visit New York City. I'm not sure where I want to go yet.

Camping in the woods will be peaceful. There will be lots of open space, fresh air, and the smell of pine around us. We can hike in the woods, swim in the pond, and play games all day. We'll fall asleep to the chirping of crickets and wake to the chirping of birds. Then again, if we go camping, we may struggle with bugs and bad weather. Nothing is worse than lots of mosquito bites. Besides, if it rains, there'll be nothing to do.

If we go to New York, we can see skyscrapers, stroll through Central Park, or ride the ferry to the Statue of Liberty. If it rains, we can visit the Empire State Building, the Museum of Natural History, or the United Nations. We can also go shopping (not my first choice) or swim in the hotel's indoor pool.

New York City, of course, will be crowded and noisy. We'll breathe in car exhaust and other polluted air. Besides, spending time in the city can be expensive. We'll have to rent a hotel room, eat at restaurants, and park our car in a garage.

After dinner on Sunday, we're going to vote on where we're going. Please write with suggestions that will help me make my choice.

Your friend,
Darrius

## Comparing and Contrasting

15. How are a camping trip and a visit to New York City alike?
    - Ⓐ Both trips cost about the same amount.
    - Ⓑ Both trips offer a lot to see and do.
    - Ⓒ Both trips are peaceful.
    - Ⓓ Both trips offer plenty of ways to get fresh air.

## Comparing and Contrasting

16. What is one way that a camping trip and a visit to New York City are different?
    - Ⓐ There's no place to swim in the city.
    - Ⓑ There's less chance of bad weather in the city.
    - Ⓒ On a camping trip, it's easier to fall asleep.
    - Ⓓ There's less open space and more noise in the city.

## PART ONE: LEARN ABOUT MAKING PREDICTIONS

Read this story about Janelle. As you read, think about what might happen next in the story.

---

**First Day**

It was Janelle's first day at summer camp. She was sitting on her cot, waiting for her cabinmates to arrive. Janelle was looking forward to sleepover camp. She liked sports, crafts, and the outdoors. Still, she was nervous. She didn't know anyone and worried that she wouldn't make any friends. What if her cabinmates didn't like her? Just then, Janelle heard giggling and laughter outside. A girl called out, "Janelle, are you in there? We want to meet our new cabinmate!"

---

Think about what you read and what you already know about "first days." Make a good guess about what might happen next. Then, continue reading to see how close your guess is to what actually happens.

---

Suddenly, three girls burst into the cabin. The girls introduced themselves to Janelle and talked excitedly about the weeks ahead. Janelle breathed a sigh of relief. She knew that she would have a lot of fun with her new friends.

---

What happened next in the story was **Janelle became friendly with her new cabinmates.**

When you think about what might happen next in a reading passage, you are **making a prediction**. Making a prediction is a way of using clues from a reading passage, as well as things you already know, to make a good guess about what might happen next.

★ Clues are often in the title of a reading passage. Read the title, and then make a prediction about what you will be reading.

★ Clues are often in the facts and details in a reading passage. Details about the things characters do and say often help you make a prediction about what they might do or say later in the story.

★ Clues are often in any pictures included with a story. Pictures often show something that is happening or will happen soon.

Read this story about an Irish couple. As you read, ask yourself, "What does the title tell me about what I will be reading? Which facts and details will help me predict what will happen next?" Then answer the questions.

**A Fisherman's Sweater**

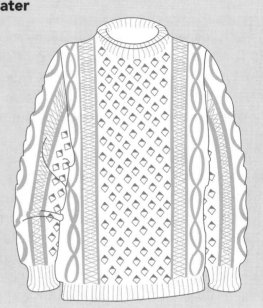

Long ago, on the green island of Ireland, a woman named Nancy lived with her husband, Ian. They lived by the blue Atlantic in a cozy stone cottage with a thatched roof. Six days a week, Ian rowed his fishing boat out to sea. Nancy stayed at home doing chores. When she had time, she knitted sweaters for Ian. Each sweater had a bold pattern.

One stormy day, Ian did not return on time. Nancy watched for him at the cottage window. She was afraid that Ian had drowned.

At last, she saw someone in the distance. A man was walking toward the cottage. Nancy strained her eyes to see who it was. The man wore a sweater. Nancy recognized the pattern immediately.

1. What do you think will most likely happen next?
   A) Nancy will see Ian's face and run outside to greet him.
   B) Another fisherman will bring news that Ian has drowned.
   C) A stranger will appear and ask for shelter from the storm.
   D) A friend who has a sweater similar to Ian's will come to visit Nancy.

2. Where did you find clues to help you make your prediction?
   A) in the title of the story
   B) in the picture that was included with the story
   C) in the details about Ian's job
   D) in the details about the sweaters that Nancy knitted

Work with a partner. Talk about your answers to questions 1 and 2. Tell why you chose the answers you did.

**Remember:** Making a prediction is a way of using clues from a reading passage, as well as things you already know, to make a good guess about what might happen next.

★ Look for clues in a reading passage to help you predict what might happen next. Clues are often in the title, in the facts and details, and in any pictures.

★ Ask yourself, "What do I already know about the things I am reading about?"

**Read this Greek myth about Achilles. As you read, look for clues that will help you predict the ending of the myth. Then answer the questions.**

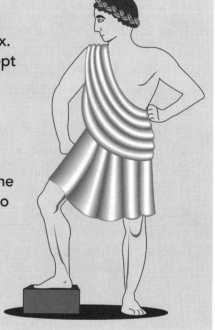

Achilles was a famous Greek warrior during the Trojan War. He was the son of the sea goddess Thetis. When Achilles was an infant, Thetis dipped him into the magical waters of the River Styx. Thus, every part of Achilles' body was protected from harm, except for one spot. This weak spot was the heel by which Thetis had held him.

When Achilles was young, he had to make a difficult choice. He could choose between a long, but ordinary, life or a short, but heroic, one. Achilles chose the second.

Achilles grew up to be a brave warrior and a loyal friend. But he was also famous for his bad moods. In one battle, Achilles got into an argument. He stomped off the battlefield. While he was gone, his best friend, Patroclus, was killed by the Trojan hero Hector. Achilles was filled with guilt and rage. He killed Hector. When Hector's brother, Paris, heard about the death, he immediately sought revenge.

3. What probably happened to Achilles?
   Ⓐ He remained safe from harm.
   Ⓑ He killed Paris.
   Ⓒ Paris killed him by wounding him in the heel.
   Ⓓ He refused to fight ever again.

4. How might things have been different if Achilles had not left the battlefield?
   Ⓐ Achilles might still be living today.
   Ⓑ Patroclus might not have died.
   Ⓒ Patroclus probably would have killed Hector.
   Ⓓ Paris would have become Achilles' friend.

**Look at the answer choices for each question. Read why each answer choice is correct or not correct.**

3. What probably happened to Achilles?

   Ⓐ He remained safe from harm.

   *This answer is not correct because clues in the story suggest that Achilles' life was in danger. He not only had a weak spot on his heel, but he also had chosen a short, but heroic, life.*

   Ⓑ He killed Paris.

   *This answer is not correct because, although both men were enemies, it was more likely that Paris would have killed Achilles. Achilles had already sought his revenge for the death of Patroclus by killing Hector. Paris was still seeking revenge against Achilles for killing his brother.*

   ● Paris killed him by wounding him in the heel.

   *This answer is correct because Paris sought revenge for his brother's death, and Achilles' only weak spot was his heel.*

   Ⓓ He refused to fight ever again.

   *This answer is not correct because Achilles was famous for his bravery and determination. He was not likely to stop fighting.*

4. How might things have been different if Achilles had not left the battlefield?

   Ⓐ Achilles might still be living today.

   *This answer is not correct because the story states that Achilles had chosen a short, but heroic, life. Besides, the weak spot on his heel would have prevented him from living forever.*

   ● Patroclus might not have died.

   *This answer is correct because if Achilles had been present on the battlefield, Hector might not have killed Patroclus. The story states that Achilles was "a brave warrior and a loyal friend." This clue suggests that Achilles would have fought courageously to protect his friend's life.*

   Ⓒ Patroclus probably would have killed Hector.

   *This answer is not correct because there are no clues to suggest that Patroclus would have killed Hector if Achilles had stayed on the battlefield.*

   Ⓓ Paris would have become Achilles' friend.

   *This answer is not correct because Paris was a Trojan. He was one of the enemies whom Achilles was fighting against. The two men were unlikely to become friends.*

★ Look for clues in the reading passage that tell what the characters are like. Think about how the characters behave, how they are feeling, and the things they say and do.

★ Link the clues with what you know from your own experiences. Ask yourself, "What have people like this character done in a similar situation?"

**Read this legend about Robin Hood. Then answer the questions.**

Long ago in England, there was a bold outlaw named Robin Hood. He lived in Sherwood Forest with his band of merry men. Robin Hood was considered a hero by many. He stole from the rich and gave what he stole to the poor.

King Henry of England ordered the sheriff of Nottingham to arrest Robin Hood. The sheriff tried to think of a trick to draw Robin Hood out of hiding. He knew that Robin Hood was quite skilled with his bow and arrow. So, the sheriff decided to have an archery contest. The grand prize would be an arrow made of pure gold.

When Robin Hood heard about the contest, he made plans to go. His merry men warned him that the sheriff was laying a trap, but Robin Hood was not afraid. On the day of the contest, he disguised himself as a beggar. He dressed in rags and wore a patch over one eye. He dyed his blond beard brown. No one recognized the stranger, not even the sheriff.

The beggar ended up being one of the three best archers. On the archers' last turn, only the beggar's arrow landed in the very center of the target. With much fuss, the sheriff congratulated the winner and handed him the golden arrow.

5. What do you think the beggar did next?
   Ⓐ He refused the prize.
   Ⓑ He accused the sheriff of being a fool.
   Ⓒ He accepted the prize and left quickly.
   Ⓓ He removed his disguise and revealed who he really was.

6. Which clue first hints that Robin Hood might win the contest?
   Ⓐ Robin Hood was a bold outlaw.
   Ⓑ Robin Hood was quite skilled with his bow and arrow.
   Ⓒ Robin Hood was not afraid of the sheriff.
   Ⓓ No one recognized Robin Hood in his disguise.

7. If the sheriff later called Robin Hood a coward for not participating in the contest, Robin Hood would probably
   Ⓐ demand an apology.
   Ⓑ send the sheriff a message saying who really won the prize.
   Ⓒ tell the sheriff that he disagreed with him.
   Ⓓ ignore the insult because of his fear of the sheriff.

8. If the sheriff discovered later who the beggar was, he would most likely
   Ⓐ be furious that he had been tricked.
   Ⓑ accept that the beggar had won the contest fairly.
   Ⓒ confess his mistake to the king.
   Ⓓ admit that Robin Hood was very clever.

**Read this book review by a fourth-grade student. Then answer the questions.**

Margaret Bourke-White by Catherine A. Welch is a biography about the life of this brave photographer.

The author begins with the photographer's early life. Margaret was born in 1906, in New York City. Young Margaret always liked adventure. Yet, she was afraid of many things. Her parents helped her to face her fears.

Margaret began taking photos in college to earn money. She often took great risks to get her pictures. She enjoyed doing these daring things. "The camera was her ticket to adventure," explains the author.

Margaret traveled all over the world as a photographer. She became well known for her pictures of people facing difficult situations. Much of her work appeared in Life magazine. During World War II, Margaret photographed soldiers. Her pictures showed the soldiers on the battlefield, in the air, and at sea. Nothing stopped her from getting the pictures she wanted.

When the war ended, Margaret took pictures of the German death camps. Millions of Jewish people had been killed there. This work was probably harder than anything else Margaret had ever done.

9. Predict what would have happened if Margaret had not been willing to take risks.
   - Ⓐ Her parents would have been angry with her.
   - Ⓑ She would never have become well known.
   - Ⓒ She would not have become a photographer.
   - Ⓓ She would not have finished college.

10. During World War II, a torpedo struck a ship that Margaret was traveling on. What do you think she did next?
   - Ⓐ She ran toward the lifeboats immediately.
   - Ⓑ She kept snapping pictures until the last possible moment.
   - Ⓒ She was so afraid that she couldn't do anything.
   - Ⓓ She stopped working for Life magazine.

11. Predict how people reacted to Margaret's photographs of the death camps.
   - Ⓐ They were shocked by what they saw.
   - Ⓑ They were angry at her for showing them the truth.
   - Ⓒ They demanded that she stop taking such horrible pictures.
   - Ⓓ They told her that a woman didn't belong in the camps.

12. What will the reviewer most likely write about in the next paragraph?
   - Ⓐ additional biographies by Catherine A. Welch
   - Ⓑ other women photographers
   - Ⓒ Margaret's life until her death, in 1971
   - Ⓓ life in Germany after the war

★ A test question about making a prediction may ask you to make a good guess about what will happen next in a reading passage, or what might happen in the future.

★ A test question about making a prediction usually contains the words *predict*, *probably*, or *most likely*.

**Here is a newspaper article about a peculiar event. Read the article. Then do Numbers 13 and 14.**

| The Daily Galaxy | Special Edition | July 19, 1963 |
|---|---|---|

SUTTON, NH—A couple from Sutton, New Hampshire, claim that they were kidnapped by aliens last week. Martin and Roz Well were driving home around midnight on Wednesday. Suddenly, they were blinded by a strong white light. They stopped their car and got out. In the sky overhead, they saw a saucer-shaped object. Seconds later, the Wells were sucked up into the "flying saucer." The next thing they knew, they were surrounded by aliens. The Wells described them as small gray creatures. They had egg-shaped heads and big, dark eyes.

The Wells can't remember any other details about being on board the spaceship. After what seemed like only a few minutes, they were released. However, they later discovered that they had been gone for five days.

Every year, hundreds of people report seeing strange objects in the sky. Most sightings turn out to be ordinary aircraft, weather balloons, or natural wonders such as clouds or shooting stars. Stories about visitors from outer space usually prove false. So far, police have been unable to find any evidence of a spacecraft near Sutton.

## Making Predictions

13. Predict how people will most likely react to the Wells' story.

   Ⓐ Most people will say the story is true.

   Ⓑ Most people will say the story was made up.

   Ⓒ Most people will claim that they too were kidnapped by aliens.

   Ⓓ Most people will be afraid to leave their homes at night.

## Making Predictions

14. Predict which of these will most likely happen if someone provides proof that a flying saucer appeared near Sutton.

   Ⓐ Police will insist that the object was a weather balloon.

   Ⓑ No one will search for additional evidence.

   Ⓒ Astronauts will search for the object in space.

   Ⓓ The Wells will receive a lot of attention for a while.

Here is a story about a boy's first experience on ice skates. Read the story. Then do Numbers 15 and 16.

Roberto was usually a confident kid. He was good at most things he did. Right this moment, though, Roberto wasn't feeling so sure about himself. Today was the day he had agreed to go ice-skating with his best friend, David.

Until last year, Roberto lived in Florida, where the weather was too warm to freeze lakes and ponds. Few towns had indoor rinks. So, the only skating Roberto ever did was on in-line skates. He loved the feeling of speeding across the pavement. He was fast, but always in control. He hoped that his skill on ice skates would prove to be as good as his skill on in-line skates.

Roberto and David walked in the crisp, cold air to the local indoor rink. Roberto sighed deeply before opening the door. The moment of truth was finally here. Would he leave as a proud skater or as an embarrassed failure? David promised Roberto that he'd be with him every step, or slip, of the way.

Roberto laced up his skates and wobbled over to the edge of the rink. He took a deep breath and stepped onto the ice. Roberto stood there for a while, holding onto the boards. Finally, he gathered up his courage and took a step forward. Then another. And another. He decided he was ready to try stepping forward and gliding on one foot. Roberto took off, lost his footing, and fell down. David grabbed him under the arms and picked him up. Roberto tried again. He fell again. And again. And again. But Roberto was determined to do better. He kept on trying.

**Making Predictions**

15. Predict what Roberto will most likely do next.
    Ⓐ He will give up and take off his skates.
    Ⓑ He will skate awhile without falling.
    Ⓒ He will ask David to stop helping him.
    Ⓓ He will sit on the ice and refuse to get up.

**Making Predictions**

16. Predict what will probably happen if Roberto goes ice-skating again.
    Ⓐ He'll refuse to go with David.
    Ⓑ He'll watch everyone else skate.
    Ⓒ He'll enjoy skating and do well.
    Ⓓ He'll wish he'd never agreed to skate.

## PART ONE: READ A FOLKTALE

Here is a folktale from Africa. Read the folktale. Then do Numbers 1 through 6.

An old man had three sons. When they had grown into manhood, he called them together. He ordered them to go out and bring him food and clothing, since he was no longer able to provide for himself.

The three brothers set out. After a very long while, they came to a large river. They decided that once they got across, they would each go separate ways. Then, in a year's time, they would come back to the same spot.

So the brothers parted. At the end of the year, they found their way back to the riverside. The oldest brother asked the youngest brother what he had found during his travels. The boy replied, "I have a mirror. If you look into it, you can see all over the country."

When the second brother was asked what he had found, he replied, "I have a pair of sandals. If one puts them on, one can walk at once to any place in the country in one step."

Then the oldest brother said, "I have a small bag of medicine, that is all. But let us look into the mirror and see how our father is."

The three brothers looked into the mirror and saw that their father was dead. The oldest brother said, "Let us hurry home and see what we can do."

So the second brother brought out his sandals, and all three placed their feet inside them. Immediately, they raced to their father's grave. Then the oldest brother shook the medicine out of its bag and poured it over the grave.

At once their father arose. It was as if nothing had been the matter with him.

## Recognizing Cause and Effect

1. Which clue word signals the reason that the old man sent his sons away?

    Ⓐ if

    Ⓑ so

    Ⓒ since

    Ⓓ because

## Recognizing Cause and Effect

2. What happened when the three brothers first looked into the mirror?

    Ⓐ They raced to their father's grave.

    Ⓑ They saw that their father was old and frail.

    Ⓒ They returned to the river.

    Ⓓ They saw that their father was no longer alive.

## Comparing and Contrasting

3. How were the oldest brother and the youngest brother alike?

    Ⓐ Both cared about their father.

    Ⓑ Both found their treasure in the same spot.

    Ⓒ Both liked practicing magic tricks.

    Ⓓ Both knew a lot about medicine.

## Comparing and Contrasting

4. How were the sandals different from the medicine bag?

    Ⓐ Only the sandals had magical power.

    Ⓑ Only the medicine in the bag could bring the father back to life.

    Ⓒ Only the younger brother could use the medicine bag.

    Ⓓ Only the medicine bag was found during the brothers' travels.

## Making Predictions

5. What will most likely happen next?

    Ⓐ The father will ask his sons to show him what they found on their journey.

    Ⓑ The father will tell the sons that he must rest for several days.

    Ⓒ The sons will leave once more in search of other magical objects.

    Ⓓ The sons will beg their father's forgiveness for being away so long.

## Making Predictions

6. If the father sent his sons off for food and clothing once more, they would probably

    Ⓐ demand that their father take care of himself.

    Ⓑ return to the same spot at the large river.

    Ⓒ spend a year searching for food and clothing.

    Ⓓ use the magic mirror and sandals during their search.

Here is an article about tasty inventions. Read the article.
Then do Numbers 7 through 12.

### Tasty Mistakes

Many of today's inventions were the result of many years of hard work and sleepless nights. Some discoveries, however, were the result of an accident. Many of these accidents had delicious results!

The invention of potato chips is one example of a tasty mistake. One day in 1853, there was an unhappy diner at a restaurant in Saratoga Springs, New York. He kept sending his fried potatoes back to the kitchen. He demanded that they be cut thinner and fried longer. Eventually, the cook, George Crum, got annoyed with the diner's complaints. Angrily, he sliced the potatoes very, very thin. Then he fried them until they were curly crisps. Last, he salted them. To Crum's surprise, the diner ate all of the crispy, salted potatoes and even asked for more. Today, these thin, crispy potatoes are called potato chips. They are also the most popular snack food in the United States.

Until the 1904 World's Fair in St. Louis, ice cream was always served in dishes. One hot day, a man selling ice cream at the fair ran out of bowls. The man next to him was selling waffles. The waffle seller quickly rolled up into a cone shape one of the thin waffles. Then he filled it with a scoop of ice cream. The ice-cream seller continued to sell ice cream in these new holders. Today this treat is known as the ice-cream cone.

An 11-year-old boy from California accidentally invented another cold treat. One night in 1905, Frank Epperson mixed up a drink. It was made with sugared powder and soda water. Then he left the drink on his back porch. The stirring stick was still in it. The temperature dropped overnight, and the mixture froze. The next morning, the boy found a stick of frozen soda water instead of his drink. Eighteen years later, Frank started a business that produced iced pops on a stick. These frozen treats were sold in seven fruit flavors. In time, they came to be called Popsicles.

## Recognizing Cause and Effect

7. The potato chip was invented because
   Ⓐ a chef wanted to create a new food using potatoes.
   Ⓑ a waiter accidentally cut some potatoes too thin.
   Ⓒ a customer liked to eat crispy foods.
   Ⓓ a cook was annoyed with a diner's complaints.

## Recognizing Cause and Effect

8. The ice-cream seller ran out of dishes, so he
   Ⓐ asked the waffle seller what to do.
   Ⓑ scooped the ice cream into cone-shaped waffles.
   Ⓒ stopped selling ice cream.
   Ⓓ served the ice cream in paper cups.

## Comparing and Contrasting

9. In what way is a Popsicle different from an ice-cream cone?
   Ⓐ A Popsicle is more popular on a hot day.
   Ⓑ The Popsicle was invented before the ice-cream cone.
   Ⓒ A Popsicle is a hand-held treat.
   Ⓓ A Popsicle is made of frozen water, not frozen cream.

## Comparing and Contrasting

10. How were Frank Epperson and George Crum alike?
    Ⓐ Both invented a frozen treat.
    Ⓑ Neither of them planned to create a popular snack.
    Ⓒ Both lived in California.
    Ⓓ Both were careless inventors.

## Making Predictions

11. Predict how visitors to the St. Louis World's Fair would have reacted to the first ice-cream cones.
    Ⓐ They demanded that their ice cream be served in dishes.
    Ⓑ They said that they'd rather have a Popsicle.
    Ⓒ They never ate ice cream in a dish again.
    Ⓓ They were eager to try this new, tasty treat.

## Making Predictions

12. Earmuffs were invented in 1873 by a young boy from Maine. Predict which of these most likely led to the invention.
    Ⓐ The boy was afraid of loud noises.
    Ⓑ The boy was tired of having cold ears every time he went skating.
    Ⓒ The boy was entering a contest for young inventors.
    Ⓓ The boy was annoyed by the sounds of life in a busy city.

## PART ONE: LEARN ABOUT FINDING WORD MEANING IN CONTEXT

**Read this paragraph about Craig. As you read, think about
the meaning of the word *indisposed* in the second sentence.**

> On what would have been his first day of a new job, Craig did
> not feel well. He had to call his boss to say that he was indisposed.
> Craig couldn't believe his bad luck. What a day to be ill!

You can figure out the meaning of the word *indisposed* by looking at the words and
phrases around it. The word *ill* and the phrase *did not feel well* are clues to the meaning
of the word *indisposed*.

**The meaning of the word *indisposed* is "unwell or ill."**

When you use clues in a reading passage to figure out the meaning of a new word, you
are **finding word meaning in context**. The words and phrases around a new word often
provide clues to the word's meaning. These clues are called **context clues**.

★ Context clues are often in the sentence where the new word appears.
   They can also be in the sentences before and after the word.

★ Clues about the meaning of a new word are often found by thinking about
   the way the word is used in the sentence.

★ Clues about the meaning of a new word can be found by thinking about
   the facts and details in the paragraph where the new word is found.

**Read this article about diamonds. As you read, ask yourself, "What clues will I use to figure out the meaning of the word** *clarity*?**" Then answer the questions.**

Diamonds are the world's hardest material. Most diamonds formed deep inside the earth about three billion years ago. Lava from volcanoes eventually carried the crystal stones to the earth's surface.

Diamonds are the most highly prized stone. However, they vary greatly in quality. The value of a diamond depends on its color, clarity, cut, and weight.

Most natural diamonds are colorless. Some diamonds, though, have elements that give them color. So, diamonds can also be red, yellow, pink, brown, green, or blue.

A diamond's clarity is what makes it sparkle brightly or appear dull. Diamonds with good clarity are easy to see through. Diamonds with poor clarity are not easy to see through. The way a diamond is cut helps show off its brightness. The better the cut, the more it shines.

Not all diamonds are used for jewelry. Most diamonds are too small or oddly shaped. But they are still valuable. Diamonds are used to make products such as computer chips. They are also used for cutting strong materials such as rock, glass, steel, and other diamonds.

1. In paragraph four, the word *clarity* probably means
   Ⓐ "colorfulness."
   Ⓑ "hardness."
   Ⓒ "dullness."
   Ⓓ "clearness."

2. Which phrase gives a clue to the meaning of the word *clarity*?
   Ⓐ sparkle brightly or appear dull
   Ⓑ most highly prized stone
   Ⓒ have elements that give them color
   Ⓓ the more it shines

 Work with a partner. Talk about your answers to questions 1 and 2. Tell why you chose the answers you did.

**Remember:** The words and phrases around a new word often give clues about the word's meaning.

★ Look for context clues in the sentence where the word appears. Look also in the sentences before and after the new word.

★ Look for clues about the meaning of a new word by thinking about the way the word is used in the sentence.

★ Look for clues about the meaning of a new word by thinking about the facts and details in the paragraph where the new word is found.

**Read this poem about a fussy eater. As you read, think about how you will figure out the meaning of any new words. Then answer the questions.**

**I Don't Like It**
*by Jeffie Ross Gordon*

I don't like spaghetti.
To me it looks like worms.
And I don't like asparagus.
I think it might have germs.
Carrots cooked are mushy.
Raw, they are too hard.
Worse than all the others
Is stuff they call Swiss chard.

Mushrooms make me queasy.
Tomatoes make me sick.
Lunch meat is too skinny.
Peanut butter is too thick.
Bacon is so greasy.
And liver, not one bite.
But give me ice cream any time.
Any flavor is all right.

3. You can tell that Swiss chard is a kind of
   Ⓐ fruit.
   Ⓑ vegetable.
   Ⓒ noodle.
   Ⓓ meat.

4. What is the best meaning of the word *queasy* in the poem?
   Ⓐ "afraid"
   Ⓑ "fatty or oily"
   Ⓒ "sick to one's stomach"
   Ⓓ "worried"

**Look at the answer choices for each question. Read why each answer choice is correct or not correct.**

3. You can tell that Swiss chard is a kind of

   Ⓐ fruit.

   *This answer is not correct because when the speaker talks about Swiss chard, there are no words or phrases that describe fruit.*

   ● vegetable.

   *This answer is correct because the words and phrases around the words Swiss chard describe vegetables—asparagus, carrots, and mushrooms. You can figure out that Swiss chard is probably a vegetable too.*

   Ⓒ noodle.

   *This answer is not correct because the word spaghetti, the only word that describes a kind of noodle, is found at the beginning of the poem, long before Swiss chard appears in the poem.*

   Ⓓ meat.

   *This answer is not correct because the words and phrases that describe different kinds of meats—lunch meat, bacon, liver—do not appear around the words Swiss chard.*

4. What is the best meaning of the word *queasy* in the poem?

   Ⓐ "afraid"

   *This answer is not correct because no words or phrases tell that the speaker is afraid of mushrooms. The speaker just doesn't like eating them.*

   Ⓑ "fatty or oily"

   *This answer is not correct because the words and phrases in the poem do not tell about fatty or oily foods.*

   ● "sick to one's stomach"

   *This answer is correct because the word sick in the next line of the poem gives a clue about the word's meaning.*

   Ⓓ "worried"

   *This answer is not correct because no words or phrases tell that the eater is worried about eating mushrooms. It's clear that the person is strongly against eating them.*

★ Look for a synonym, a word with a similar meaning, near a new word in a reading passage.

★ Look for an antonym, a word with an opposite meaning, near a new word in a reading passage.

★ Once you think you know the meaning of a new word, read the sentence where the word appears, using this new meaning. Does the sentence still make sense in the story? If so, you've probably figured out the meaning of the new word.

**Read this story about a brave lighthouse keeper. Then answer the questions.**

### A Beacon of Hope

Lookout Lighthouse was located on an island off the coast of Maine. The 75-foot tower had a powerful signal light at the top. The flashing light was used to guide ships and warn them of the rocky islands nearby.

Most days, calm waters surrounded the lighthouse. But June 10 was not like most days. By sunrise, black clouds had rolled in. A harsh wind began whipping up turbulent waves. By noon, a furious storm swirled round the lighthouse.

Lea, the light keeper, watched from her post. She saw a ship drifting helplessly toward a rocky island. It was the *Star Erikson.*

Quickly, Lea raced to her boat. She rowed with all of her strength through the rough waters, and toward the troubled vessel. Three sailors had been knocked off the ship's deck into the choppy water. Lea pulled them, one by one, into her boat. Then, following its bright beacon, she rowed back to the lighthouse. Because of Lea, none of the sailors lost their life in the terrible storm.

5. In paragraph two, which clue word is an antonym of *turbulent?*

Ⓐ harsh

Ⓑ calm

Ⓒ furious

Ⓓ rocky

6. In paragraph two, which word gives a clue to the meaning of *swirled?*

Ⓐ round

Ⓑ rolled

Ⓒ surrounded

Ⓓ whipping

7. In paragraph four, which clue word is a synonym of *choppy?*

Ⓐ "bright"

Ⓑ "troubled"

Ⓒ "terrible"

Ⓓ "rough"

8. In the last paragraph, the meaning of the word *beacon* is

Ⓐ "a signal light."

Ⓑ "a message."

Ⓒ "a tower."

Ⓓ "a lookout post."

Read this article about space stations. Then answer the questions.

### Space Stations: Past, Present, and Future

Scientists believe that huge space stations orbiting Earth will provide a safe way to search the universe. The first space station was launched, in 1971, by the Soviet Union. It was called *Salyut 1*. Three cosmonauts traveled around Earth in the space station for 24 days. Sadly, the three crew members died trying to return home.

Two years later, the United States launched the *Skylab* space station. It went on three missions. A crew of three astronauts carried out each mission. The astronauts performed many important experiments on *Skylab*. Several experiments helped scientists understand how the human body acts in space.

Presently, the Russian space station *Mir* is orbiting the planet. *Mir* was launched in 1986. There are usually two cosmonauts on board. A visiting astronaut from the United States sometimes joins them.

American astronauts and Russian cosmonauts are working together to build an international space station. Crews from each country will travel into space to assemble the station. They will travel by space shuttle and complete at least 36 trips.

A six-person crew will man the space station when it is finished. The station will orbit Earth once every 90 minutes. People across the world will be able to see the station in the night sky. It will look like a bright star moving from west to east.

9. In paragraph one, you can tell that the word *orbiting* means
   - Ⓐ "exploring."
   - Ⓑ "speeding away from."
   - Ⓒ "traveling toward."
   - Ⓓ "traveling around."

10. In paragraph one, which word or words give a clue to the meaning of *cosmonauts*?
   - Ⓐ "scientists"
   - Ⓒ "universe"
   - Ⓑ "crew members"
   - Ⓓ "space stations"

11. In paragraph four, which clue word is a synonym of *assemble*?
   - Ⓐ build
   - Ⓒ orbit
   - Ⓑ travel
   - Ⓓ complete

12. In the last paragraph, the best meaning of the word *man* is
   - Ⓐ "to succeed in doing something."
   - Ⓑ "to orbit around Earth."
   - Ⓒ "to be in charge of or operate."
   - Ⓓ "to supply with equipment."

★ A test question about finding meaning in context asks you about the meaning of a word from a reading passage. The word may or may not be familiar to you. The word might also be used in a new way.

★ A test question about finding meaning in context usually has several answer choices. Try each answer choice in the sentence in which the word appears. Decide which answer choice makes the most sense in the reading passage.

**Here is a funny story from Italy. Read the story. Then do Numbers 13 and 14.**

### Giufá and the Judge

One summer, the flies in Giufá's home gave him no peace. He'd flap his hands and stamp his feet, but it didn't help.

"I'll teach you flies how to behave," he said and went to court to complain.

"What is your grievance?" asked the judge. "What has been done to you?"

"My complaint is against the flies in my house."

"Against the flies!" the judge cried. "What crime have they committed?"

"They are forever biting and stinging me. I never did any harm to them!"

The judge laughed. "Giufá, I am afraid that I can't do anything about that."

"You are the judge and must punish those who do wrong. You must not exonerate their behavior!"

"Giufá, I can't punish the flies, but I give you permission to kill any you see."

Just then, a fly, which had been buzzing about the courtroom, settled on the judge's nose. Without saying a word, Giufá made a fist and aimed a punch right at the judge's nose.

The blow killed the fly, and nearly broke the judge's nose. But the judge could do nothing. He simply sent Giufá home and told him never to appear in his courtroom again.

**Finding Word Meaning in Context**

13. In paragraph three, you can tell that the word *grievance* means
    - Ⓐ "sadness."
    - Ⓑ "praise."
    - Ⓒ "complaint."
    - Ⓓ "foolishness."

**Finding Word Meaning in Context**

14. In paragraph eight, what is the best meaning of the word *exonerate*?
    - Ⓐ "excuse"
    - Ⓑ "strike"
    - Ⓒ "correct"
    - Ⓓ "examine"

Here is an article about a place of wonder. Read the article. Then do Numbers 15 and 16.

### On Top of the World

All mountains must rise at least 2,000 feet above sea level. Otherwise, they are just hills. The highest mountain in the world is Mount Everest. It stands between Nepal and part of China. Mount Everest is part of the Himalayas, the world's highest mountain range.

Local people call Mount Everest *Chomolungma*. This name means "Goddess of the Snows." The name suits the snowy giant. Mount Everest has the highest elevation of any mountain on Earth. Its peak rises 29,108 feet (about 5 1/2 miles) above sea level!

People began trying to climb to the top of Mount Everest in the 1920s. In 1953, two men finally succeeded. Edmund Hillary, of New Zealand, and Tenzing Norgay, a guide from Nepal, became the first people to reach the summit. Since then, hundreds of people have done the same. However, many climbers have also lost their lives on route.

Mount Everest is the world's most difficult mountain to climb. Scaling it requires special clothing, equipment, and skill. The higher a climber climbs, the thinner the air becomes. Thin air is difficult to breathe, therefore climbers must breathe in bottled oxygen. Also, the slopes are covered with deep snow and thick ice. Sometimes, a large mass of snow breaks loose. It causes an avalanche that can sweep climbers down the mountain and bury them.

Another danger for climbers is the climate on top of Mount Everest. Temperatures can drop quickly, and winds can blow at speeds of 200 miles per hour.

**Finding Word Meaning in Context**

15. In paragraph two, the word *elevation* means
    Ⓐ "height above 2,000 feet."
    Ⓑ "height above sea level."
    Ⓒ "height below sea level."
    Ⓓ "height below 2,000 feet."

**Finding Word Meaning in Context**

16. In paragraph four, the meaning of the word *avalanche* is
    Ⓐ "a climber who slides down a mountain slope."
    Ⓑ "a deep crack in the ice."
    Ⓒ "a mass of snow that falls down a mountainside."
    Ⓓ "thin air that is difficult to breathe."

# STRATEGY 8

**PART ONE: LEARN ABOUT DRAWING CONCLUSIONS AND MAKING INFERENCES**

**Read this Chinese folktale about the Moon Lady. As you read, try to figure out why the Moon Lady gives whiskers to the old woman.**

Long ago in China, the Moon Lady appeared to an old woman and offered to grant her one wish. The old woman was so surprised to see the Moon Lady that she couldn't speak. Finally, the old woman moved her hand up and down over her mouth and chin. She was trying to ask the Moon Lady for a little more rice to eat. The Moon Lady looked puzzled. Yet, she promised the old woman that she would grant her wish. When the old woman looked in her bowl the next morning, it still held only a few grains of rice. But when she put her hand to her face, she found that the Moon Lady had given her whiskers!

The folktale does not tell why the Moon Lady gave whiskers to the old woman. It does, however, give you details that help you figure out why this happened.

**The Moon Lady offered to grant an old woman a wish.**

**The old woman was so surprised that she couldn't speak.**

**The old woman moved her hand up and down over her mouth and chin.**

**The Moon Lady looked puzzled.**

These details help you figure out that the Moon Lady did not understand the old woman's hand movements. The Moon Lady thought that the old woman wanted whiskers. You probably know from your own experience that it can be confusing when a person uses gestures instead of words.

Details are sometimes not clearly stated or explained in a reading passage. You must figure out some information on your own. Whenever you figure out something that is not told in a reading passage, you are **drawing a conclusion** or **making an inference**.

★ Pay attention to the details in a reading passage. You can use these details to figure out information that is not clearly stated or explained.

★ Use the details from the reading passage and what you know from your own life to draw a conclusion or to make an inference.

Read this article about the sinking of the *Titanic*. As you read, look for details that will help you figure out who survived the sinking and why. Then answer the questions.

### The *Titanic* Tragedy

On April 10, 1912, the *Titanic* set off on her first voyage. She was traveling from England to New York. The 2,207 passengers on board were filled with excitement. They were on board the finest ocean liner in the world. They were also on the first ship to be declared "unsinkable." On the evening of April 14, however, something went terribly wrong. At 11:45 P.M., the *Titanic* struck an iceberg. Within $2\frac{1}{2}$ hours, the ship had sunk, and 1,502 lives were lost.

The *Titanic* carried enough lifeboats for just 1,178 people. However, only about 700 people actually filled the boats that floated away. The crew filling the boats ordered that "women and children go first." This rule mostly helped passengers who were traveling in first class. Only 4 of 143 women in first class died that evening. In second class, 15 of 93 women did not make it. In third class, however, 81 of 179 women were lost. As for the children, all 29 in first and second class were saved. Only 23 out of 76 children in third class survived.

1. From the article, you can tell that the lifeboats were
   Ⓐ damaged and could not be used.
   Ⓑ not necessary on most ships.
   Ⓒ not completely filled with passengers when they floated away.
   Ⓓ only for those who traveled in first class.

2. Which detail from the article helped you answer question 1?
   Ⓐ Fewer men than women survived.
   Ⓑ There were more people in third class than in first class.
   Ⓒ There were enough lifeboats for 1,178 people, but only 700 filled them.
   Ⓓ Only women and children were allowed to board the lifeboats first.

 Work with a partner. Talk about your answers to questions 1 and 2. Tell why you chose the answers you did.

**Remember: Drawing a conclusion or making an inference is a way of figuring out information that is not stated in a reading passage.**

★ Think about the details that are stated in a reading passage. Use these details to help you figure out information that is not explained.

★ Use the details from the reading passage and what you know from your own life to draw a conclusion or to make an inference.

**Read this Greek myth about a proud young woman. As you read, ask yourself, "What details are explained? What information can I figure out on my own?" Then answer the questions.**

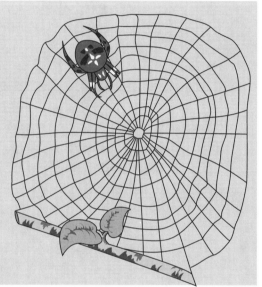

Arachne was a poor young woman from Greece. She spun the most beautiful cloth. People thought that Athena, the goddess of crafts, had taught Arachne her skill. But Arachne denied this talk. She boasted that she wove better than Athena did. She even challenged Athena to a weaving contest.

On the day of the contest, Arachne and Athena worked all day. Each woman wove many colorful cloth designs. When they had finished, Athena saw that Arachne's work really was more beautiful than her own. Athena became furious and tore up Arachne's weaving. Then she turned Arachne into a spider. Since that day, spiders have woven beautiful webs.

3. From the myth, what can you tell about Arachne?

   Ⓐ She was a shy woman.

   Ⓑ She was jealous of Athena.

   Ⓒ She was afraid of Athena.

   Ⓓ She was proud of her skill.

4. From what you have read, you can conclude that Athena was

   Ⓐ sure she would win the contest.

   Ⓑ more powerful than Arachne.

   Ⓒ better at other crafts than she was at weaving.

   Ⓓ kind toward others.

**Look at the answer choices for each question. Read why each answer choice is correct or not correct.**

**3.** From the myth, what can you tell about Arachne?

&#9312; She was a shy woman.

*This answer is not correct because there are no details in the myth that suggest Arachne was a shy woman. In fact, her boasting suggests the opposite.*

&#9313; She was jealous of Athena.

*This answer is not correct because there are no details that suggest Arachne was jealous of Athena. In fact, it was Athena who was jealous of Arachne.*

&#9314; She was afraid of Athena.

*This answer is not correct because there are no details that suggest Arachne was afraid of Athena. In fact, Arachne was quite bold to challenge the goddess to a weaving contest.*

&#9899; She was proud of her skill.

*This answer is correct because Arachne's boasting and her challenge to Athena help you figure out that she was proud of her skill.*

**4.** From what you have read, you can conclude that Athena was

&#9312; sure she would win the contest.

*This answer is not correct because there are no details in the myth that suggest Athena was certain she would win the contest.*

&#9899; more powerful than Arachne.

*This answer is correct because Athena turned Arachne into a spider. You can figure out from this detail that Athena was more powerful than Arachne.*

&#9314; better at other crafts than she was at weaving.

*This answer is not correct because there are no details about crafts other than weaving.*

&#9315; kind toward others.

*This answer is not correct because Athena did not act kindly toward Arachne. She was so jealous of Arachne that she turned her into a spider.*

★ Look for details in a reading passage that tell about how a person or character looks, acts, thinks, feels, and speaks. Think about what you know about people with similar qualities.

★ Look for details in a reading passage that suggest where or when something happens. If something happens at the White House, you can figure out that the setting is Washington, D.C. If something happens while the stars are out, you can figure out that it is nighttime.

**Read this article about winter sleepers. Then answer the questions.**

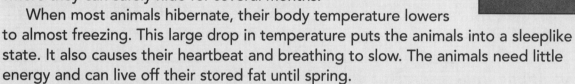

Many animals live in places where the winter is cold and harsh. There is not enough food to eat. Some animals survive the winter by going into a deep winter sleep called hibernation.

Hibernating animals prepare for their long nap in the late summer or early fall. First, they eat lots of food. This extra food is stored in their body as fat. Then they choose a warm place where they can safely hide for several months.

When most animals hibernate, their body temperature lowers to almost freezing. This large drop in temperature puts the animals into a sleeplike state. It also causes their heartbeat and breathing to slow. The animals need little energy and can live off their stored fat until spring.

Some animals wake from their sleep several times during the winter. Chipmunks, for example, get up and go out when the weather is mild. They also store real food instead of body fat. Bears usually sleep only through the worst weather in winter. Their body temperature drops only a few degrees. Therefore, they can easily awake from their sleep at any time.

5. You can tell that when animals come out of hibernation,
   Ⓐ their bodies are very cold.
   Ⓑ their body temperature rises.
   Ⓒ they have a hard time staying awake.
   Ⓓ they return to the north.

6. Details in the article suggest that hibernators
   Ⓐ know when to go to sleep and when to wake.
   Ⓑ travel to warmer places when winter comes.
   Ⓒ always store enough food to last through the winter.
   Ⓓ sleep underground.

7. From this article, what can you conclude about hibernating bears?
   Ⓐ Their body temperature is always changing.
   Ⓑ Their heart beats quicker than that of other hibernating animals.
   Ⓒ They hibernate longer than most animals.
   Ⓓ They store supplies of food in their den.

8. From the article, you can tell that
   Ⓐ few animals hibernate in winter.
   Ⓑ hibernation is the only way for animals to survive the winter.
   Ⓒ people also have a hard time in winter.
   Ⓓ only animals that live in places where winters are harsh hibernate.

**Read this legend, which takes place long ago in Britain. Then answer the questions.**

## The Sword and the Stone

Long ago, Uther Pendragon was the king of Britain. His chief magician was Merlin. Merlin used his powerful magic to help the king fight his enemies and win the hand of the beautiful Igraine. When the king and queen had their first child, Merlin warned them that their son's life would be in danger at the castle. So, Merlin took the baby into hiding.

Three years later, the king died. For the next twelve years, the lords and their knights fought over who should be the next king. Then, one winter, Merlin came out of hiding. He told the Archbishop of Canterbury to gather all the nobles together at the cathedral on Christmas Day. When they arrived, the nobles saw a stone that had been set in the churchyard. Sticking out of the stone was a large sword, with these words: *Whoever can pull the sword from this stone is the true king of Britain.*

All the knights tried to remove the sword. But not one of them could even move it. Finally, the archbishop invited all the knights in the land to a jousting tournament. After the tournament, each knight would have a chance to pull the sword from the stone.

A proud knight named Sir Kay traveled to the tournament with his younger brother, Arthur, and their father, Sir Hector. Just before the event began, Sir Kay realized that he had forgotten his sword. He ordered Arthur to go back to their inn to get it. But when Arthur got there, the doors were locked and no one answered. Everyone was at the tournament.

While he was thinking about what to do, Arthur passed the cathedral and spotted the large sword sticking out of the stone. Arthur grabbed the handle and gave it a sharp tug. The sword slid from the stone smoothly and silently.

Arthur quickly rode back to the tournament and handed the sword to Sir Kay. Sir Kay recognized the weapon and quickly hid it under his cloak.

9. From the legend, you can tell that the archbishop planned the tournament to
   Ⓐ find the strongest knight in the land.
   Ⓑ find the new king of Britain.
   Ⓒ entertain the people of Britain.
   Ⓓ show off the skills of each knight.

10. Details in the legend suggest that Merlin
    Ⓐ did not trust the archbishop.
    Ⓑ had lied about the baby's life being in danger.
    Ⓒ wanted to be the future king.
    Ⓓ had used his magic to set the stone in the churchyard.

11. From this legend, what can you conclude about Sir Kay?
    Ⓐ He was treated badly by his brother.
    Ⓑ He had forgotten his sword on purpose.
    Ⓒ He would claim that he had pulled the sword from the stone.
    Ⓓ He would win the jousting tournament.

12. You can tell that Arthur
    Ⓐ wanted to enter the tournament too.
    Ⓑ knew that Sir Hector wasn't his father.
    Ⓒ was actually King Uther's son.
    Ⓓ would also become a knight one day.

★ A test question about drawing conclusions or making inferences asks you to figure out something that is not stated in a reading passage.

★ A test question about drawing conclusions or making inferences often contains the words *you can tell, determine,* or *conclude.*

**Here is a business letter. Read the letter. Then do Numbers 13 and 14.**

1776 Conservation Way
Greenville, WI 54942
January 1, 2001

May K. Waste, President
Pretty U Cosmetics
One Landfill Place
Chicago, IL 60612

Dear Ms. Waste:

I am writing to express my concerns about the amount of packaging you use for your products. Most of this wrapping ends up being thrown away. Don't you realize that trash is a serious problem in our country! An average American family throws away more than one ton of trash a year. About 80 percent of it is buried in landfills. Often, the buried trash does not break down quickly. Plastics, especially, can remain buried in the land for hundreds of years. Shame on you!

Please begin to use less packaging for your products. Also, use materials that can be recycled. And encourage your customers to find ways to use the packaging again.

I hope you will seriously consider my suggestions. Together, we can all help save the earth.

Sincerely,
Rhea Cycle

**Drawing Conclusions and Making Inferences**

13. You can tell that the writer of the letter
   Ⓐ works at a landfill.
   Ⓑ does not wear cosmetics.
   Ⓒ is concerned about the environment.
   Ⓓ wonders why trash is such a serious problem.

**Drawing Conclusions and Making Inferences**

14. There is enough information in the letter to show that
   Ⓐ plastic breaks down more slowly than other materials.
   Ⓑ the writer's suggestions will be ignored.
   Ⓒ burning trash is better than burying it.
   Ⓓ buried trash never breaks down.

Here is a science article about asteroids. Read the article. Then do Numbers 15 and 16.

You probably know a lot about the planets that orbit the sun. But how much do you know about the asteroids, comets, and meteoroids that also zoom around our solar system?

Asteroids are chunks of rock that measure from 3,000 feet to 600 miles across. Comets are huge, icy bodies that range in size from 3,000 feet to 60 miles across. Their tails are made of gas and dust and can stretch millions of miles. Meteoroids are pieces of rock, metal, or ice. Most meteoroids have broken off from comets or asteroids. They can be as small as a grain of sand or as large as a house.

**asteroid**

If an asteroid or a comet several miles across struck Earth, the explosion would have the power of many atomic bombs. Such an event may have been the reason that the dinosaurs disappeared. Even if the object landed in the ocean, the explosion would cause so much dust that there'd be no sunlight for months. Tidal waves would destroy coastal cities.

Several movies have been made about a huge asteroid or comet speeding toward Earth. Experts try to find a way to avoid impact. One plan involves destroying the object with a bomb. In real life, blowing apart an asteroid or a comet too close to Earth would not save the planet. The blown-up bits of rock and ice would still cause damage.

The details in these disaster films are not necessarily accurate. The threat, though, of Earth's being battered from above is real. Concerned scientists, however, are always on the lookout for any real comet or asteroid that could strike Earth.

**Drawing Conclusions and Making Inferences**

15. From this article, you can tell that
    - Ⓐ asteroids and comets are always hitting Earth.
    - Ⓑ an asteroid or a comet could one day hit Earth.
    - Ⓒ blowing up asteroids and comets is a good idea.
    - Ⓓ comets that land in the ocean are not dangerous.

**Drawing Conclusions and Making Inferences**

16. From this article, you can conclude that meteoroids
    - Ⓐ can be easily destroyed by scientists.
    - Ⓑ are always visible to the human eye.
    - Ⓒ are less dangerous than asteroids.
    - Ⓓ have long tails like comets.

## PART ONE: LEARN ABOUT DISTINGUISHING BETWEEN FACT AND OPINION

**Read this paragraph about a popular snack. As you read, look for statements that can be proved. Also look for statements that tell what someone thinks or feels.**

Popcorn is the best snack to eat at fairs, movies, and ball games. I believe that popcorn is the most healthful treat. Popcorn is actually good for you, if you leave out the butter and salt. People have been popping popcorn for thousands of years. The native people in what is now Mexico were the first to grow popcorn plants. The popcorn kernels were too hard to eat. One native tossed a handful of the hard kernels into a fire. Pop! America's most tasty treat was born.

The statements that can be proved are

**Popcorn is actually good for you, if you leave out the butter and salt.**
**People have been popping popcorn for thousands of years.**
**The native people in what is now Mexico were the first to grow popcorn plants.**
**The popcorn kernels were too hard to eat.**
**One native tossed a handful of the hard kernels into a fire.**

The statements that tell what someone thinks or feels are

**Popcorn is the best snack to eat at fairs, movies, and ball games.**
**I believe that popcorn is the most healthful treat.**
**America's most tasty treat was born.**

If a statement can be proved, it is a **fact**. If a statement tells what someone thinks or feels about something, it is an **opinion**. Facts can be proved. Opinions cannot. When you figure out if a statement is a fact or an opinion, you are **distinguishing between fact and opinion**.

★ Facts are statements that can be checked or proved.

★ Opinions are statements that cannot be proved. They tell what someone thinks or feels.

★ Opinions often contain such clue words as *think, feel, believe,* and *seem.* Other common clue words are *always, never, all, none, most, least, greatest, best,* and *worst.*

Read this copy from a Web site designed for daring travelers. As you read, ask yourself, "Which statements can be proved? Which statements cannot be proved?" Then answer the questions.

---

**Polar Travel**

Back

Forward

Home

Tired of visiting the same old places? Need some excitement in your life? Ready to show just how tough you are? If you've answered yes to these questions, then we have an adventure for you. Come join Polar Travel on a flight to the North Pole. We think the North Pole is the "coolest" place on the planet!

Our pilots are the greatest in the world, and the planes we fly are the safest. It will take us ten days to reach the Pole, with stops along the way. As we cross the High Arctic, we may spot a few polar bears and people. As we get closer to the Pole, though, we'll see only miles and miles of snow and ice. (It's so cold at the North Pole that the ocean surrounding it is frozen most of the year.) This white desert is the most beautiful spot on Earth.

Our next flight to the North Pole leaves in early April. By then, it's no longer dark all the time. Also, the ice has not yet begun to thaw and crack. Our planes have special landing gear, but we don't want our icy runway to open up.

So, pack your bags and get ready to go. Make sure you pack lots of warm clothes. Nothing is as brutal as the weather in the North Pole.

---

1. Which statement is a fact?
   Ⓐ We think the North Pole is the "coolest" place on the planet!
   Ⓑ It's so cold at the North Pole that the ocean surrounding it is frozen most of the year.
   Ⓒ This white desert is the most beautiful spot on Earth.
   Ⓓ Nothing is as brutal as the weather in the North Pole.

2. Which clue word signals an opinion about the skills of Polar Travel pilots?
   Ⓐ think
   Ⓑ believe
   Ⓒ greatest
   Ⓓ most

---

Work with a partner. Talk about your answers to questions 1 and 2. Tell why you chose the answers you did.

**Remember: Facts can be proved. Opinions cannot be proved.**

★ To find out if a statement is a fact, ask yourself, "Can this statement be proved?"

★ To find if a statement is an opinion, ask yourself, "Does this statement tell what someone thinks or feels?"

★ Look for clue words that signal an opinion, such as *think, feel, believe, seem, always, never, all, none, most, least, greatest, best,* and *worst.*

**Read this article about a terrible event in history. As you read, think about which statements are facts and which statements are opinions. Then answer the questions.**

During the Middle Ages, the people in Europe forgot what their ancestors had known about staying healthy. No one worried about having a fresh water supply. No one cared about removing waste from the streets. No one took baths anymore. With these unclean conditions, diseases spread quickly. When a disease broke out, it often killed thousands of people. The worst of these epidemics was known as the Black Death. It first hit Europe in 1348.

Rats first carried the disease that caused the Black Death. Most of these pests had come to Europe on ships. Everyone lived in constant fear that death could strike them down at any time. In just three years, 25 million people died. In 25 years, the Black Death killed between one third and one half of Europe's entire population. Europeans have never known a sadder time in their history.

3. Which of these statements about the Middle Ages can be proved?

Ⓐ No one cared about removing waste from the streets.

Ⓑ No one took baths anymore.

Ⓒ When a disease broke out, it often killed thousands of people.

Ⓓ Everyone lived in constant fear that death could strike them down at any time.

4. Which of these statements tells what someone thinks or feels?

Ⓐ The Black Death first hit Europe in 1348.

Ⓑ Rats first carried the disease that caused the Black Death.

Ⓒ In just three years, 25 million people died.

Ⓓ Europeans have never known a sadder time in their history.

Look at the answer choices for each question. Read why each answer choice is correct or not correct.

3. Which of these statements about the Middle Ages can be proved?

Ⓐ No one cared about removing waste from the streets.

*This answer is not correct because it cannot be proved that no one cared about removing waste. Most likely, some people did care.*

Ⓑ No one took baths anymore.

*This answer is not correct because it cannot be proved that no one took baths. People must have washed up every now and then; some more often than others.*

● When a disease broke out, it often killed thousands of people.

*This answer is correct because you can prove this statement is true. You can find facts about what happened when diseases broke out during the Middle Ages in a book, on a CD-ROM encyclopedia, or on the Internet.*

Ⓓ Everyone lived in constant fear that death could strike them down at any time.

*This answer is not correct because, though people may have lived in constant fear of dying, it's doubtful that everyone was afraid all of the time.*

4. Which of these statements tells what someone thinks or feels?

Ⓐ The Black Death first hit Europe in 1348.

*This answer is not correct because this statement is a fact, which can be proved. You can find facts about the Black Death in a book, on a CD-ROM encyclopedia, or on the Internet.*

Ⓑ Rats first carried the disease that caused the Black Death.

*This answer is not correct because this statement is a fact, which can be proved. You can find facts about the Black Death in a book, on a CD-ROM encyclopedia, or on the Internet.*

Ⓒ In just three years, 25 million people died.

*This answer is not correct because this statement is a fact, which can be proved. You can find facts about the Black Death in a book, on a CD-ROM encyclopedia, or on the Internet.*

● Europeans have never known a sadder time in their history.

*This answer is correct because it states what the writer believes to be the saddest time in European history. It cannot be proved. The clue word never signals that this statement is an opinion, not a fact.*

★ Facts can be observed, checked, or tested. You can prove that a fact is correct or true.

★ Opinions express someone's thoughts, feelings, or beliefs. An opinion can be about an event, an idea, a person, or a thing. Even though a person might agree or disagree with an opinion, it still cannot be proved.

**Read this report about Jim Thorpe. Then answer the questions.**

Jim Thorpe was born in Oklahoma on May 28, 1888. He lived with his family on an Indian reservation. Jim's Native-American name was *Wa-Tho-Hack*. This means "bright path." Jim's parents chose this name just for their son. They believed he had a promising future.

Jim always liked to play sports. He ran in races and played football and baseball. Jim was an excellent athlete. He showed great talent in every sport he played. I think Jim was the most amazing athlete. He was so good at so many sports. Jim didn't really think about his future until he was in college. That's when he decided to play sports for a living. He went on to win gold medals in the 1912 Olympics in Sweden. Sweden's king called Jim "the greatest athlete in the world." Jim had finally found his bright path. He became one of the best athletes ever.

5. Which of these is a fact from the report?
   Ⓐ Jim ran in races and played football and baseball.
   Ⓑ Jim was an excellent athlete.
   Ⓒ Jim became one of the best athletes ever.
   Ⓓ I think Jim was the most amazing athlete.

6. Which of these statements cannot be proved?
   Ⓐ He was so good at so many sports.
   Ⓑ Jim Thorpe was born in Oklahoma on May 28, 1888.
   Ⓒ Jim's Native-American name was *Wa-Tho-Hack*.
   Ⓓ He went on to win gold medals in the 1912 Olympics in Sweden.

7. Which of these clue words signals an opinion of Sweden's king?
   Ⓐ most
   Ⓑ best
   Ⓒ greatest
   Ⓓ believed

8. A fact about Jim Thorpe that can be proved is
   Ⓐ he lived with his family on an Indian reservation.
   Ⓑ he was the greatest athlete in the world.
   Ⓒ he was so good at so many sports.
   Ⓓ he became one of the best athletes ever.

Read this movie review written by a student for her weekly school newspaper. Then answer the questions.

## This Week's Video Pick

*Star Wars* is the best movie ever made. There's something to please everyone in this science-fiction flick. George Lucas is the creator of *Star Wars*. I think that George Lucas is a genius. He has the greatest imagination. He has invented the most amazing characters, robots, spaceships, and special effects.

Millions of people have seen *Stars Wars*. It's one of the top five movies in ticket and rental sales. On the day the film was released in May 1977, people lined up for hours at theaters to see it. When the movie ended, some people got right back in line.

The movie's plot is about the fight between the Rebel Alliance and the evil Empire. The Rebel princess holds stolen plans for the Death Star. The Death Star is the battle station that Darth Vader wants to build. Darth Vader is the leader of the Empire and he wants the stolen plans back. When the princess's ship is attacked, she hides the plans in a robot called R2D2. Princess Leia is captured, but R2D2 escapes with C3P0, a fellow droid, to the planet Tatooine. There they meet Luke Skywalker. R2D2 leads the young man to an old man named Obi-Wan Kenobi. Obi-Wan is a former Jedi knight. He is also the wisest of men. He tells Luke about Darth Vader, the most dreaded member of the Empire, and teaches Luke the ways of the Force. Next, Luke and Obi-Wan hire a big furry beast named Chewbacca and a bold pilot named Han Solo to help them. They need to deliver the Death Star plans to the Rebel Alliance before Darth Vader can get the plans back.

I won't reveal the rest of the story, just in case you are one of the few people who haven't seen it. If you haven't seen *Star Wars*, rent it today. Seeing the film is an experience you won't forget. May the force be with you!

9. Which of these statements about George Lucas can be proved?
   Ⓐ I think that George Lucas is a genius.
   Ⓑ He has invented the most amazing characters, robots, spaceships, and special effects.
   Ⓒ George Lucas is the creator of *Star Wars*.
   Ⓓ He has the greatest imagination.

10. Which of these is a fact from the movie review?
   Ⓐ *Star Wars* is one of the top five movies in ticket and rental sales.
   Ⓑ There's something to please everyone in this science-fiction flick.
   Ⓒ *Star Wars* is the best movie ever made.
   Ⓓ Seeing the film is an experience you won't forget.

11. Which of these statements is an opinion about Obi-Wan Kenobi?
   Ⓐ Obi-wan is a former Jedi knight.
   Ⓑ He teaches Luke Skywalker the ways of the Force.
   Ⓒ He is also the wisest of men.
   Ⓓ He tells Luke Skywalker about Darth Vader.

12. Which of these is an opinion about Darth Vader?
   Ⓐ He is the leader of the Empire.
   Ⓑ He is the most dreaded member of the Empire.
   Ⓒ He wants to build the Death Star.
   Ⓓ He wants the stolen plans back.

DISTINGUISHING BETWEEN FACT AND OPINION

★ A test question about distinguishing between fact and opinion may ask you to identify which of four statements is a fact or an opinion.

★ To recognize a fact, read each answer choice, and ask yourself, "Can this statement be proved?" If it can, then it is a fact.

★ To recognize an opinion, read each answer choice, and ask yourself, "Does this statement tell what someone thinks or feels?" If it does, then it is an opinion. Look for clue words in the answer choices that signal an opinion.

**Here is a student's report on penguins. Read the report. Then do Numbers 13 and 14.**

> The penguin is the most unusual bird. It walks upright and cannot fly. I think the penguin is the funniest-looking bird in the world. With its black back and white belly, it looks like a small, round waiter wearing a tuxedo. The penguin must be the clumsiest animal on land. It waddles about on two short legs and webbed feet.
>
> Although penguins walk funny and can't fly, they are excellent swimmers. Penguins are more graceful in the water than any other sea animal. Instead of wings, penguins have powerful flippers. They help penguins swim underwater at fast speeds.
>
> Penguins live in cold waters in the Southern Hemisphere. Several kinds live in Antarctica, the coldest place on Earth. Penguins have many layers to protect them from freezing temperatures. Thick layers of fat under thick skin help keep in heat. A thick coat of short, oily feathers keeps their skin dry. Beneath this waterproof coat are downy feathers. They trap warm air around the body.
>
> There are 18 kinds of penguins. The largest is the emperor penguin. It stands about four feet high and weighs about 100 pounds. It has a collar of bright orange and yellow feathers around its neck. In 1997, scientists in Antarctica discovered an all-white emperor penguin. So far, this rare penguin is the only one of its kind to be seen.

**Distinguishing Between Fact and Opinion**

13. Which of these is an opinion from the report?
    - Ⓐ Penguins live in cold waters in the Southern Hemisphere.
    - Ⓑ The largest penguin is the emperor penguin.
    - Ⓒ The penguin waddles about on two short legs and webbed feet.
    - Ⓓ I think the penguin is the funniest-looking bird in the world.

**Distinguishing Between Fact and Opinion**

14. Which of these is a fact from the report?
    - Ⓐ The penguin must be the clumsiest animal on land.
    - Ⓑ Penguins have many layers to protect them from freezing temperatures.
    - Ⓒ Penguins are more graceful in the water than any other sea animal.
    - Ⓓ The penguin is the most unusual bird.

Here is a news story about a historic event. Read the news story.
Then do Numbers 15 and 16.

**World News**             **July 21, 1969**

# Men Land on Moon!

Last night at 10:56 Eastern Daylight Time, astronaut Neil Armstrong became the first person to set foot on the moon. About 600 million TV viewers witnessed the moon landing. It was the proudest moment in United States history. As Armstrong placed his left foot onto the moon's surface, he told the world, "That's one small step for man, one giant leap for mankind." His words will be remembered always.

Minutes later, Edwin "Buzz" Aldrin, Jr., joined Armstrong on the moon's surface. The third crew member, Michael Collins, remained in orbit aboard the command ship, *Columbia*.

Armstrong and Aldrin are the bravest people alive. They explored the moon for more than two hours. They planted an American flag on the moon's surface. They also took pictures, set up experiments, and collected soil and rock samples.

Armstrong, Aldrin, and Collins blasted off from Cape Kennedy in *Apollo 11* on July 16.

The spacecraft traveled at the speed of 35,533 feet per second. Altogether, it took 103 hours and 30 minutes to travel from Earth to the moon.

On July 20, Armstrong and Aldrin went down to the moon's surface in their lunar module, the *Eagle*. They landed on the Sea of Tranquillity. This sea has no water. It is named for one of the flat, dark areas on the moon.

The *Apollo 11* astronauts plan to return to Earth on July 24. They'll probably receive the best homecoming anyone has ever had. It is believed that these three men will become heroes to every child in the nation.

## Distinguishing Between Fact and Opinion

15. Which of these is a fact from the news story?

   Ⓐ Armstrong, Aldrin, and Collins blasted off from Cape Kennedy in *Apollo 11* on July 16.

   Ⓑ Armstrong's words will be remembered always.

   Ⓒ Armstrong and Aldrin are the bravest people alive.

   Ⓓ It is believed that these three men will become heroes to every child in the nation.

## Distinguishing Between Fact and Opinion

16. Which of these is an opinion from the news story?

   Ⓐ Armstrong became the first person to set foot on the moon.

   Ⓑ Armstrong and Aldrin explored the moon for more than two hours.

   Ⓒ About 600 million TV viewers witnessed the moon landing.

   Ⓓ It was the proudest moment in United States history.

## PART ONE: READ A JOURNAL ENTRY

**Here is an entry from Aaron's journal. Read the journal entry.
Then do Numbers 1 through 6.**

*Monday, October 13*

Today was the best day! A new boy joined our class. His name is Paul, and I've never met a nicer kid. Our teacher had told us last week that Paul was coming from a place very far away. I thought he would probably have very different customs. When Paul walked into our classroom this morning, though, he looked just like any other boy in the class. He wore a T-shirt and jeans. His sneakers were just like the ones I was wearing.

Then Paul spoke. Although he used English, I had trouble understanding him. Paul has the most unusual accent, and he uses expressions that I've never heard before.

When Paul introduced himself to the class, he said "G'day" for "Good day." Paul told us that he liked many of the same sports as American boys and girls, or as Paul says, "blokes" and "sheilahs." He has a younger brother in the first grade, and Paul told us that the little "nipper" is the biggest pest. Paul also explained that his family's flight to the States was the bumpiest plane ride ever. He felt "crook" during the entire flight.

Finally, I asked Paul the question everyone wanted answered. "Where are you from?"

"I'm from Oz," answered Paul.

"Hey, Mr. Wizard," someone called out, "have you ever met the Lion, the Tin Man, or the Scarecrow?"

Everyone laughed, including Paul. "I must have kangaroos in my top paddock!" he exclaimed. "What I meant to say is that I'm from Australia."

## Finding Word Meaning in Context

1. You can tell that the word *sheilahs* in paragraph three means
   Ⓐ "brothers."
   Ⓑ "girls."
   Ⓒ "kangaroos."
   Ⓓ "very young children."

## Finding Word Meaning in Context

2. In paragraph three, the word *crook* probably means
   Ⓐ "bent."
   Ⓑ "delighted."
   Ⓒ "ill."
   Ⓓ "selfish."

## Drawing Conclusions and Making Inferences

3. From the journal entry, you can tell that
   Ⓐ Paul has a sense of humor.
   Ⓑ Paul doesn't like to be teased.
   Ⓒ Paul hates to fly in airplanes.
   Ⓓ Paul's favorite sport is soccer.

## Drawing Conclusions and Making Inferences

4. Which detail from the story helped you answer question 3?
   Ⓐ Paul told us that the little "nipper" is the biggest pest.
   Ⓑ Paul told us that he liked many of the same sports as American boys and girls.
   Ⓒ I asked Paul the question everyone wanted answered.
   Ⓓ Everyone laughed, including Paul.

## Distinguishing Between Fact and Opinion

5. Which clue word signals an opinion about Paul's accent?
   Ⓐ think
   Ⓑ best
   Ⓒ never
   Ⓓ most

## Distinguishing Between Fact and Opinion

6. Which of these is a fact?
   Ⓐ Paul's younger brother is the biggest pest.
   Ⓑ Paul's flight to the States was the bumpiest plane ride ever.
   Ⓒ Paul dresses like the other boys in his class.
   Ⓓ Paul is the nicest kid.

Here is a short biography of a famous president. Read the biography.
Then do Numbers 7 through 12.

You know that George Washington was the first
president of the United States. He was in office from
1789 to 1797. You probably also know that he was a
general in the American Revolution. Here are some
facts, though, that you may not know.

Washington was a wise man. Yet, he never went
to college. Washington went to school near the
Virginia farms where he grew up. He took his first job
at age 17.

In his early twenties, Washington fought to protect
the frontier against the French and the Indians.
Washington was a reckless soldier. During one battle, he was particularly
careless. Two horses were shot from under him, and four bullets pierced
his coat. But he rode on unharmed. Later, Washington became our nation's
bravest general.

Washington was a very tall man for his time. Some people thought he
appeared stiff and unfeeling. In truth, Washington always treated others
with warmth and kindness.

Washington liked things to be just so. Mount Vernon, his plantation
where he often experimented with new crops, always looked beautiful.
Washington rode in the fanciest carriages pulled by the finest horses. He
also dressed in elegant clothes. Even his false teeth were the best he could
get. They were made from the tusk of a hippopotamus.

Washington chose the site for the capital later named in his honor. But
he never governed there. He led the country from New York City during
his first term. He governed from Philadelphia during his second term.

Washington always did his best, but he was never hungry for power. In
1782, it was suggested that General Washington become king. He said no
immediately. He also later refused a third term as president.

In 1799, Washington died suddenly. He was 67 years old. After his death,
a friend delivered a speech to Congress. It summed up the great leader's
contributions to the new nation: "Washington was first in war, first in peace,
and first in the hearts of his countrymen."

## Finding Word Meaning in Context

7. In paragraph three, which phrase gives a clue to the meaning of the word *reckless*?

Ⓐ . . . our nation's bravest general.

Ⓑ . . . fought to protect the frontier . . .

Ⓒ . . . was particularly careless.

Ⓓ . . . rode on unharmed.

## Drawing Conclusions and Making Inferences

10. From the biography, you can tell that

Ⓐ Washington was easily embarrassed.

Ⓑ Washington's teeth caused him a lot of pain.

Ⓒ Washington didn't like living in New York City.

Ⓓ Washington never lived in the White House.

## Finding Word Meaning in Context

8. In paragraph five, the word *plantation* means

Ⓐ "a large farm."

Ⓑ "a home on a mountain."

Ⓒ "a beautiful garden."

Ⓓ "the capital of Virginia."

## Distinguishing Between Fact and Opinion

11. Which of these statements is an opinion?

Ⓐ Mount Vernon was the name of Washington's plantation.

Ⓑ Washington became our nation's bravest general.

Ⓒ Washington had false teeth.

Ⓓ Washington chose the site of our nation's present capital.

## Drawing Conclusions and Making Inferences

9. There is enough information in the biography to show that Washington

Ⓐ was a modest man.

Ⓑ was stern with the soldiers under his command.

Ⓒ was a foolish man.

Ⓓ regretted that he didn't go to college.

## Distinguishing Between Fact and Opinion

12. Which of these is a fact?

Ⓐ Washington should not have been so careless.

Ⓑ Washington always did his best.

Ⓒ Washington did not want to be king.

Ⓓ Washington was the best American president.

## PART ONE: LEARN ABOUT IDENTIFYING AUTHOR'S PURPOSE

Read this nonsense poem about a frog. As you read, think about
why the author probably wrote the poem.

**The Frog**

What a wonderful bird the frog are—
When he stand he sit almost;
When he hop, he fly almost.
He ain't got no sense hardly;
He ain't got no tail hardly either.
When he sit, he sit on what he ain't got almost.

*Anonymous*

The author probably wrote the poem to make you smile or laugh.
The author's purpose is to entertain readers with a silly poem.

All authors write for a reason. The reason an author writes something is called the
author's purpose. When you figure out why a reading passage was written, you are
**identifying the author's purpose**. Authors write for one of four reasons—to describe,
to entertain, to explain, or to persuade.

★ Some reading passages mainly describe something, such as a person, place, or thing.
The author's purpose is to **describe**.

★ Some reading passages mainly tell a personal story, tell something funny, or use a story
to teach a lesson. The author's purpose is to **entertain**.

★ Some reading passages mainly tell how to do something, or contain lots of information
about a person, place, or thing. The author's purpose is to **explain**.

★ Some reading passages are mainly written to try to get readers to do something,
buy something, or believe something. The author's purpose is to **persuade**.

Read this article about newspapers. As you read, try to figure out
the author's purpose for writing the article. Then answer the questions.

**What's News?**
Many people start their morning by reading the newspaper.
The newspaper is filled with ads, comics, and news articles. Some news
articles are written to tell readers about important events. These events
may take place in the community, across the nation, and around
the world.

Another purpose of newspapers is to describe things. News articles
often supply lots of details about events, people, or places.

Another purpose of newspapers is to persuade readers. The
editorial pages are filled with writers' opinions. Writers try to convince
people to think or feel the same way. Ads are found throughout the
newspaper. Ads try to get people to buy goods.

Newspapers also have fun things to entertain readers. Comic strips
and word puzzles are popular with readers.

1. The author wrote the article mainly to
   (A) explain what is found in a newspaper.
   (B) describe how a newspaper is made.
   (C) try to get readers to buy the daily newspaper.
   (D) entertain readers with an enjoyable story about newspapers.

2. You know your answer to question 1 is correct because the article mainly
   (A) provides facts or tells readers how to do something.
   (B) contains many details that describe something.
   (C) tries to convince readers of something.
   (D) tells an enjoyable story.

 Work with a partner. Talk about your answers to questions 1 and 2.
Tell why you chose the answers you did.

**Remember: Authors write to describe, to entertain, to explain, or to persuade.**

★ To figure out if the author's purpose is to describe, ask yourself, "Does the author provide lots of details about a particular person, place, or thing?"

★ To figure out if the author's purpose is to entertain, ask yourself, "Does the author tell a personal story or try to make me laugh? Does the author use a story to teach a lesson?"

★ To figure out if the author's purpose is to explain, ask yourself, "Does the author tell me facts about a person, place, or thing? Does the author tell me how to do or make something?"

★ To figure out if the author's purpose is to persuade, ask yourself, "Does the author try to get me to do something, buy something, or believe something?"

**Read this ad from a travel brochure. As you read, ask yourself, "Why did the author probably write this ad?" Then answer the questions.**

### Come to Jamaica!

Come visit the beautiful island of Jamaica. Nowhere else will you find so many natural wonders. Jamaica has miles and miles of soft, sandy beaches. There are also forests, mountains, rivers, and spectacular waterfalls. Not surprisingly, the island's name means "land of wood and water."

While you are here, you will enjoy day after day of warm weather. Jamaica has a tropical climate, so there are no cold seasons. Don't miss the chance to shop at the exciting outdoor marketplaces. Or just listen to the rhythm of Jamaican "talk." Whatever you decide to do, Jamaica is the place for you.

3. The author wrote the ad mainly to
   Ⓐ persuade readers to go to Jamaica.
   Ⓑ explain the history of Jamaica.
   Ⓓ describe Jamaica's major products.
   Ⓒ entertain readers with tales about Jamaica.

4. You know your answer to question 3 is correct because the ad mainly
   Ⓐ contains many details that describe something.
   Ⓑ provides facts or tells readers how to do something.
   Ⓒ tries to convince readers of something.
   Ⓓ tells an enjoyable story.

Look at the answer choices for each question. Read why each answer choice is correct or not correct.

3. The author wrote the ad mainly to

● persuade readers to go to Jamaica.

*This answer is correct because the ad contains lots of convincing reasons that people should visit the island.*

Ⓑ explain the history of Jamaica.

*This answer is not correct because the ad does not contain facts or other information that explains the history of Jamaica.*

Ⓒ describe Jamaica's major products.

*This answer is not correct because the ad does not contain any details that describe Jamaica's major products.*

Ⓓ entertain readers with tales about Jamaica.

*This answer is not correct because the ad does not tell an interesting story or try to make readers laugh, nor does the author use a story to teach a lesson.*

4. You know your answer to question 3 is correct because the ad mainly

Ⓐ contains many details that describe something.

*This answer is not correct because the ad does not mainly contain many details that describe a particular person, place, or thing.*

Ⓑ provides facts or tells readers how to do something.

*This answer is not correct because the ad does not mainly provide many facts or tell readers how to do something.*

● tries to convince readers of something.

*This answer is correct because the ad contains mainly opinions about Jamaica's beauty. These details are provided to convince people that Jamaica is the place to go for a beautiful and warm vacation spot.*

Ⓓ tells an enjoyable story.

*This answer is not correct because the ad does not tell an interesting story or try to make readers laugh, nor does the author use a story to teach a lesson.*

Different reading passages are written for different purposes. Knowing the kind of passage you are reading often helps you identify the author's purpose.

★ Articles are usually written to describe or explain. Some articles describe a person, place, or thing. Others explain something, such as how a simple machine works or what it means to be a good student.

★ Directions are written to explain.

★ Personal stories, riddles, and poetry are written to entertain.

★ Ads and articles in which an opinion is stated are written to persuade.

**Read each passage. Then answer the questions.**

**I          Come One, Come All**
**Who:**    Anyone who is a kid at heart
**What:**   First Annual Sandcastle Contest
**Where:**  Sunset Beach
**When:**   August 8 (Rain date August 15)
**Why:**    To have fun and maybe win a trip to the sandy beaches of Aruba!
**How:**    Bring pails and shovels, and let your imagination go!

**II          Sand Art**
Gather spoons, a paintbrush, a glass jar, and bags of nontoxic, colored sand. Spoon thin layers of sand into the jar. Spread each sand layer evenly with the paintbrush. Work carefully to avoid mixing colors. To vary the design, press the end of the paintbrush against the jar and push down. The sand will move down, forming a pattern with points.

**III          Just for Laughs**
What do you call a grouchy person at the beach?
*A sand crab.*

What did the ocean say to the sand?
*Nothing; it just waved.*

**IV          Quicksand**
Quicksand is loose, wet sand. It can be found near the mouths of rivers and along beaches. Quicksand forms when water flows upward from deep in the ground. The bubbling water pushes the sand grains apart so that they flow like water. Contrary to what most people believe, quicksand does not pull things down into it. The best thing to do if caught in quicksand is to float on top of it.

5. The author's main purpose in passage I is to
   Ⓐ describe.          Ⓒ entertain.
   Ⓑ explain.           Ⓓ persuade.

6. The author's main purpose in passage II is to
   Ⓐ describe.          Ⓒ entertain.
   Ⓑ explain.           Ⓓ persuade.

7. The author's main purpose in passage III is to
   Ⓐ describe.          Ⓒ entertain.
   Ⓑ explain.           Ⓓ persuade.

8. The author's main purpose in passage IV is to
   Ⓐ describe.          Ⓒ entertain.
   Ⓑ explain.           Ⓓ persuade.

Read this notice, which appeared on a school bulletin board.
Then answer the questions.

**Save the Florida Manatee!**

The human population in Florida is growing, but the manatee population is dying out. People are taking over this sea mammal's habitat. In fact, the gentle creature has no enemies, except for people.

The manatee looks like a huge potato with flippers and a tail. Actually, this large, lumbering creature is a cousin to the elephant. Manatees can reach 15 feet in length. They can weigh up to 1,600 pounds.

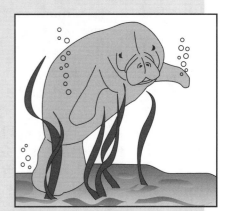

Manatees live in warm, shallow waters and graze on water plants. The animals are too big to move quickly, so boats often hit them. Speeding boats kill more than 100 manatees every year. Curious people also put the manatee in danger. Manatees are shy about being watched. They'll swim out to deeper, colder waters, where it is harder to survive.

Many people are working hard to protect the Florida manatee. New laws have lowered the speed limits for boats in manatee habitats. In at least 20 of these warm-water areas, no boats are allowed. You can help too. Write a letter to the governor of Florida stating your interest in saving the manatee. Act now, before the manatee disappears forever.

9. The author wrote paragraph one mainly to
   A explain what is happening to manatees.
   B persuade readers to stay out of Florida.
   C describe how manatees behave.
   D entertain readers with a myth about a manatee.

10. The author wrote paragraph two mainly to
   A tell where manatees live.
   B convince readers that manatees are related to elephants.
   C describe what a manatee looks like.
   D entertain readers with a funny comparison.

11. The author wrote paragraph three mainly to
   A describe boating accidents.
   B explain why manatees are in danger.
   C persuade readers to help protect manatees.
   D amuse readers with a tale about curious people.

12. The author wrote paragraph four mainly to
   A explain boating rules in manatee habitats.
   B persuade readers to help save the manatee.
   C describe how laws are made.
   D explain why the manatee is disappearing.

★ A test question about identifying the author's purpose may ask you why an author probably wrote a particular reading passage. This kind of question is asking about the purpose of the entire reading passage.

★ A test question about identifying the author's purpose may ask you why a particular paragraph was written. This kind of question is asking about only one part of the reading passage.

**Here is a story about a fussy man. Read the story. Then do Numbers 13 and 14.**

A man went into a bakery and ordered a German-chocolate cake. "I'm very particular," he told the baker. "The cake must be in the shape of the letter *B*. Can you do that for me?"

"It won't be easy," the baker answered. "I'll have to make the cake by hand, and it will take three days. But I'm sure you'll be happy with it."

Three days later, the man returned. But when he saw his cake, his face fell. "I'm sorry," he said. "It's not your fault, but I can't accept this cake. I guess I forgot to mention that it has to be in the shape of a lowercase *b*. I'll pay you anyway, but would you please try again?"

"It's your money," said the baker with a sigh. "It'll take another three days, but I want my customers to be happy."

Three days later, the customer came back. "The cake looks wonderful," he said. "It's exactly what I wanted."

"Great," replied the baker. "Let me put it in a box for you."

"That's all right," the man said. "I'll eat it here."

**Identifying Author's Purpose**

13. What is the author's purpose in the first paragraph?
    Ⓐ to describe what the man wanted
    Ⓑ to explain why the man wanted a *B*-shaped cake
    Ⓒ to make readers hungry for German-chocolate cake
    Ⓓ to amuse readers with details about a man's fussy ways

**Identifying Author's Purpose**

14. The author wrote this story mainly to
    Ⓐ explain why the baker was eager to please his customer.
    Ⓑ describe a man with a sweet tooth.
    Ⓒ convince readers that it's not good to be too fussy.
    Ⓓ entertain readers with a ridiculous story.

Here is an imaginary interview with the scientist Marie Curie. Read the interview. Then do Numbers 15 and 16.

| | |
|---|---|
| **Interviewer:** | Dr. Curie, please tell us about your early years. |
| **Dr. Curie:** | I was born in Poland in 1867. At age 15, I finished school. Girls in Poland were forbidden to go to the university, so I decided to move to a country where I was free to study. |
| **Interviewer:** | Where did you go, and when did you arrive there? |
| **Dr. Curie:** | I went to Paris in 1891 to study science at the Sorbonne. I worked hard and became the top student in my class. |
| **Interviewer:** | What led you to the discovery that made you famous? |
| **Dr. Curie:** | In 1896, Antoine-Henri Becquerel discovered that the metal uranium gave off strange and powerful rays. I decided to find out what these rays could do. I began working with a soft rock that contained uranium. I found that the rock contained another interesting material. This element gave off rays more powerful than uranium's. My husband, Pierre, and I worked together to separate this element from the rock. In 1902, we succeeded. We named the new element radium. In 1903, we were awarded the Nobel Prize in physics for our discovery. In 1911, after my husband's death, I also received the Nobel Prize in chemistry. |

## Identifying Author's Purpose

15. The author uses an interview format mainly to
   (A) describe the events that shaped Marie Curie's life.
   (B) inform readers about the dangers of radium.
   (C) try to get people excited about studying science.
   (D) entertain readers with stories about Marie Curie.

## Identifying Author's Purpose

16. What is the main purpose of the last part of the interview?
   (A) to convince readers that Pierre Curie also worked hard
   (B) to describe for readers the events before and after the Curies' discovery
   (C) to show readers that Marie Curie was proud
   (D) to delight readers with a tale about a Nobel Prize winner

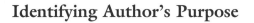

## PART ONE: LEARN ABOUT INTERPRETING FIGURATIVE LANGUAGE

Read this sentence. As you read, think about the two things being compared.

> **The clouds looked like white sheep in the sky.**
>
> The two things being compared are clouds and sheep.
> The writer used a **simile** to help readers picture how fluffy the clouds were.
> A simile uses the word *like* or *as* to compare two things.

Read this sentence. As you read, think about the two things being compared.

> **Falling leaves are orange clowns doing somersaults.**
>
> The two things being compared are falling leaves and orange clowns.
> The writer used a **metaphor** to help readers picture the sight of the falling leaves.
> A metaphor compares two things but does not use the word *like* or *as*.
> A metaphor says that one thing *is* another thing.

Now read this sentence. As you read, think about the meaning of the underlined words.

> **Henry realized that he'd just <u>put his foot in his mouth</u>.**
>
> The underlined words mean that Henry said something he shouldn't have said.
> The underlined words are an **idiom**.
> An idiom is a phrase whose words have a meaning different from their usual meaning.

Similes, metaphors, and idioms are types of figurative language. Authors use figurative language to help readers create pictures in their mind. When you understand the meaning of a simile, a metaphor, or an idiom, you are **interpreting figurative language**.

★ Look for things that are compared in a reading passage. Try to find examples of similes or metaphors.

★ Look for phrases whose words have a meaning different from their usual meaning. Try to find examples of idioms.

★ Figurative language usually brings a picture to a reader's mind. Use that picture to help you understand the meaning of the figurative language.

Read this selection from a poem by Lucy Larcom. As you read, ask yourself, "What pictures come to mind?" Then answer the questions.

## In Time's Swing
### by Lucy Larcom

Father Time, your footsteps go
Lightly as the falling snow.
Singing merrily, let me swing
Out of winter into spring.

Swing me out, and swing me in!
Trees are bare, but birds begin.
April chased off March today;
Now I catch a glimpse of May.

Oh, the smell of sprouting grass!
In a blur the violets pass.
Swing me low, and swing me high,
To the warm clouds of July.

Slower now, for at my side
White pond lilies open wide.
Crickets in the grass I hear;
Asters light the fading year.

Slower still! October weaves
Rainbows of the forest leaves.
Oh, 'tis snowing, swing me fast,
While December shivers past!

Frosty-bearded Father Time,
Stop your footfall on the rime!
While you swing me—gently, do!—
From the Old Year to the New.

1. In the poem, Father Time's footsteps are compared to
   Ⓐ crickets in the grass.
   Ⓑ forest leaves blowing in the wind.
   Ⓒ birds softly chirping.
   Ⓓ falling snow.

2. In the second stanza, the phrase *catch a glimpse* means
   Ⓐ "chase something."
   Ⓑ "see something briefly."
   Ⓒ "act like a bully."
   Ⓓ "see a dim light."

 Work with a partner. Talk about your answers to questions 1 and 2. Tell why you chose the answers you did.

**Remember:** Similes, metaphors, and idioms are types of figurative language. Authors use figurative language to help readers create pictures in their mind.

★ Look for things that are compared in a reading passage.

★ Look for phrases whose words have a meaning different from their usual meaning.

★ Think about any pictures that come to mind as you read. Use those pictures to help you understand what is being described.

**Read this fable from Aesop. As you read, look for things that are compared. Also look for words that have a meaning different from their usual meaning. Then answer the questions.**

### The Dog and the Wolf

A dog was lying in the sun in front of a farmyard gate. Suddenly, a wolf pounced upon the dog and was about to eat him up. The dog, though, begged for his life.

"Look at me," the dog told the wolf. "I am as thin as a rail. What a wretched meal I should make you now. In a few days, my master will be giving a feast. I'll be able to pick and choose among the table scraps. I shall get nice and fat. Then will be a better time for you to eat me."

The wolf thought this was a very good plan and went away. Sometime afterwards, he came to the farmyard again. There he found the dog lying out of reach on the stable roof.

"Come down and be eaten," the wolf called. "Have you forgotten our agreement?"

But the dog said coolly, "My friend, if ever you should catch me lying down by the gate again, don't wait for any feast."

Moral: *Once bitten, twice shy.*

3. In paragraph two, the dog's thinness is compared to
   Ⓐ table scraps.
   Ⓑ a cat.
   Ⓒ a wolf.
   Ⓓ a rail.

4. The moral of the story is *once bitten, twice shy*. The phrase *once bitten, twice shy* means that someone who
   Ⓐ is very shy should avoid getting bitten.
   Ⓑ faced danger in the past is more careful in the future.
   Ⓒ was bitten once becomes twice as shy.
   Ⓓ bites is twice as shy as other individuals.

**Look at the answer choices for each question. Read why each answer choice is correct or not correct.**

**3.** In paragraph two, the dog's thinness is compared to

Ⓐ table scraps.

*This answer is not correct because there is no comparison between the dog and table scraps.*

Ⓑ a cat.

*This answer is not correct because the paragraph doesn't mention a cat, nor does it suggest that the dog's thinness is like a cat's.*

Ⓒ a wolf.

*This answer is not correct because the dog's thinness is not compared to a wolf.*

● a rail.

*This answer is correct because the dog actually says in the paragraph that he is as* thin *as a rail. The word* as *signals that two things are being compared in a simile.*

**4.** The moral of the story is *once bitten, twice shy.* The phrase *once bitten, twice shy* means that someone who

Ⓐ is very shy should avoid getting bitten.

*This answer is not correct because there are no details in the fable to hint at this meaning of the phrase. Neither animal in the story is shy, nor is either bitten.*

● faced danger in the past is more careful in the future.

*This answer is correct because the details in the fable suggest that after facing the possibility of becoming the wolf's meal by lying in an unsafe place, the dog later protects himself by lying out of reach on the stable roof.*

Ⓒ was bitten once becomes twice as shy.

*This answer is not correct because there are no details in the fable to hint at this meaning of the phrase. Neither animal in the story is bitten, nor is either shy.*

Ⓓ bites is twice as shy as other individuals.

*This answer is not correct because there are no details in the fable to hint at this meaning of the phrase. Neither animal in the story is shy, and neither animal bites.*

★ Think about the things being compared in a simile or a metaphor. Ask yourself, "What do the two things have in common?" This will help you create pictures in your mind.

★ Look at the sentences near an idiom. You might find context clues to help you figure out its meaning.

**Read this tall tale about a remarkable woman. Then answer the questions.**

### Sally Ann Thunder Ann Whirlwind Crockett

Long ago on the Tennessee frontier, there lived a woman named Sally Ann. She was married to Davy Crockett, who called her his sweet little wife. Sally Ann, however, wasn't exactly sweet or little. She had a quick temper and looked daggers at anyone who upset her. Sally Ann stood as tall as a young tree and had arms as big as a woodcutter. She liked to wear a bearskin for a dress and a hornet's nest for a bonnet. Her toothpick was a bowie knife.

People said that Sally Ann was made of thunder with a dash of whirlwind thrown in for good measure. So, she became known as Sally Ann Thunder Ann Whirlwind Crockett. Sally Ann walked like an ox and ran like a fox. She could wade the wide Mississippi without getting wet. She could jump over the Grand Canyon with both eyes shut. Furthermore, she could blow out the moonlight, ride a panther bareback, sing a wolf to sleep, and jump over her own shadow. Sally Ann also had a big sense of humor. She could laugh the bark off a pine tree.

Sally Ann feared nothing. But she never bragged. And she never fought any person or creature for no good reason.

5. In the first paragraph, the phrase *looked daggers at* means
   Ⓐ "pointed at silently."
   Ⓑ "stared at curiously."
   Ⓒ "glared at angrily."
   Ⓓ "glanced at quickly."

6. The tall tale says that Sally Ann *ran like a fox*. This means that Sally Ann was
   Ⓐ fast.
   Ⓑ sly.
   Ⓒ strong.
   Ⓓ quiet.

7. Sally Ann's height is compared to that of
   Ⓐ a woodcutter.
   Ⓑ the Grand Canyon.
   Ⓒ a bear.
   Ⓓ a young tree.

8. In paragraph two, what does the phrase *for good measure* mean?
   Ⓐ "finding the correct amount by measuring"
   Ⓑ "in addition to a certain amount"
   Ⓒ "a helpful measuring tool"
   Ⓓ "a generous amount"

**Read this song about a hardworking cowboy. Then answer the questions.**

## The Cowboy Song

All day on the prairie
    in a saddle I ride,
Not even a dog, boys,
    to trot by my side.
My fire I must kindle
    with chips gathered round,
And boil my own coffee
    without being ground.
My bread lacking leaven
    I bake in a pot,
And I sleep on the ground
    for want of a cot.

I wash in a puddle
    and wipe on a sack,
I carry my wardrobe
    along on my back.
My ceiling's the sky,
    my carpet the grass,

My music the lowing
    of herds as they pass.
My books are the brooks,
    my sermons the stones,
My **parson's** a wolf
    on a pulpit of bones.

**parson:** a minister or preacher

9. In the song, the sky is compared to the cowboy's
   - Ⓐ ceiling.
   - Ⓑ carpet.
   - Ⓒ parson.
   - Ⓓ fire.

10. Which two things are compared in the song?
   - Ⓐ the cowboy's sermons and music
   - Ⓑ the cowboy's cot and the grass
   - Ⓒ the cowboy's wardrobe and a sack
   - Ⓓ the cowboy's music and the lowing of herds

11. The phrase *my books are the brooks* means that the cowboy
   - Ⓐ got his books wet.
   - Ⓑ soaks up written words like water.
   - Ⓒ studies the brooks as he would study books.
   - Ⓓ reads by the water.

12. Which of these is a metaphor?
   - Ⓐ I boil my own coffee without being ground.
   - Ⓑ My bread lacking leaven I bake in a pot.
   - Ⓒ I carry my wardrobe along on my back.
   - Ⓑ My parson's a wolf on a pulpit of bones.

★ A test question about interpreting figurative language may ask you about the meaning of a simile, a metaphor, or an idiom.

★ A test question about interpreting figurative language may ask you about things that are compared in the reading passage.

**Here is a newspaper ad. Read the ad. Then do Numbers 13 and 14.**

## Too Busy? Call Busy Bees!

Is the clutter in your house driving you up a wall? Are you going bananas thinking about everything you need to do? Is never having enough time bugging you? If you're ready to throw in the towel, let Busy Bee do it for you. We'll do your laundry and lots more too.

There's no job Busy Bees won't do. We clean homes and offices inside and out. We walk dogs and feed fish. We buy groceries and cook meals. We wash cars and water lawns. We return purchases and library books. We even help kids with their homework.

Other businesses can't hold a candle to Busy Bees. Our workers are as quick as lightning and as quiet as mice.

Don't be afraid to admit you need help. Come clean and call Busy Bees today. We'll go all out to help you.

**Interpreting Figurative Language**

13. In the ad, the workers' quickness is compared to
  Ⓐ books.
  Ⓑ mice.
  Ⓒ lightning.
  Ⓓ bees.

**Interpreting Figurative Language**

14. The phrase *can't hold a candle to* means
  Ⓐ "are not careful about causing fires."
  Ⓑ "are not as good as."
  Ⓒ "are not quick as lightning."
  Ⓓ "are not as bright as."

Here is a tall tale. Read the tale. Then do Numbers 15 and 16.

### The Popcorn Patch

"I had an old mule once upon a time that fooled himself clean to death," said Hank Huggins. "It happened down in Cade's Cove where I had planted me a little patch of corn, the kind that's used for popping. It was a hot day. I didn't want to go out plowing that morning, but my wife got after me. . . . Once my wife has set her mind to something, there's no peace until it's done. So I went out, hitched up the mule, and set off to plow the cornfield.

"Heavens to Betsy, it was hot in that cove! The mountains standing up all around kept out every breath of breeze. The place held the heat like an oven. July flies were a-droning in the trees and the leaves hung as limp as a dog's tongue. It would be hard to say which was hotter, me or that old mule. Up and down the rows we went, a-toiling and a-sweating.

"Along towards noon it was broiling for certain. Even the old logs and stumps began to crawl off in the shade. Suddenly, I heard a crackling sound in the air. Before I could figure out what had happened, white flakes were a-flying all around. At first, I thought it was a snowstorm. Then I realized what it was: The blazing sun had set that corn a-popping, and it was falling like a snowstorm.

"That old mule of mine, he stopped and looked around. Then he began to shiver. He thought for sure he'd been overtaken by a howling blizzard. He stood there and squinched himself all up, like critters do when it's real cold.

" 'Get along there!' I hollered at him. 'It's nothing but popcorn!'

"But the poor thing couldn't understand. He'd never seen any popcorn before and he thought it was snow. He just stood there, shaking and shivering in every limb. I couldn't do a thing with him. It was a crying shame. Before I could get that critter unhooked from the plow and out of there, he gave right up. He lay down in the row and froze to death—all covered up with popcorn."

## Interpreting Figurative Language

15. The phrase *set her mind to something* means that Hank's wife
    - Ⓐ never stops thinking.
    - Ⓑ becomes determined.
    - Ⓒ likes to nag.
    - Ⓓ asks others for favors.

## Interpreting Figurative Language

16. In the tall tale, the falling popcorn is compared to
    - Ⓐ cornstalks.
    - Ⓑ a mountain.
    - Ⓒ snowflakes.
    - Ⓓ a dog's tongue.

## PART ONE: LEARN ABOUT DISTINGUISHING BETWEEN REAL AND MAKE-BELIEVE

**Read this story about an unusual dog. As you read, think about the things that could really happen and the things that could not really happen.**

> A dog walks by a Western Union office. He decides to go inside to send a telegram. A clerk is standing behind the counter. The dog asks the clerk for a form. The dog then takes a pen in his teeth and slowly writes his message: Bow wow wow, bow wow wow, bow wow.
>
> The clerk reads the message and counts the words. The clerk says, "Are you aware that your telegram has only eight words? You can send ten words for the same price. Perhaps you'd like to add another 'bow wow'?"
>
> "I could," the dog replies, "but don't you think that would sound just a little ridiculous?"

The things that could really happen

**A dog walks by a Western Union office.**
**A clerk is standing behind the counter.**
**The clerk reads the message and counts the words.**

The things that could not really happen

**The dog decides to go inside to send a telegram.**
**The dog asks the clerk for a form.**
**The dog then takes a pen in his teeth and slowly writes his message.**
**The dog and clerk have a conversation.**

Things you read that could happen in real life are **real.** Things you read that could not happen in real life are **make-believe.** When you figure out which parts of a reading passage are real and which parts are make-believe, you are **distinguishing between real and make-believe.**

★ Real stories are about events that could really happen.

★ Make-believe stories are about events that could not really happen. Clues that signal a story is make-believe are unlikely or magical events, imaginary places, talking animals, and characters who do impossible things.

★ Often, some parts of a story are real, and other parts are make-believe.

Read this story about a girl named Keiko. As you read, think about which things in the story could really happen and which things could not really happen. Then answer the questions.

### Monster of the Deep

Keiko was lying in bed. She had just finished reading in her encyclopedia about the giant squid. This fierce creature exists way down deep in the dark, cold sea. The giant squid is 70 feet long and weighs several tons. Its eyes are the size of dinner plates. It has ten arms and a beak like a parrot. No one has ever seen a giant squid alive. Giant squids are not found in the part of the ocean where people swim or go boating. Keiko shuddered at the thought of meeting one. Keiko was still thinking about the giant squid when she drifted off to sleep.

Keiko was in a boat enjoying a day on the ocean when a giant arm, or tentacle, reached overboard. The tentacle was covered with rows of suckers. Keiko had read that the suckers hold the squid's food as the tentacles carry it to the mouth. She didn't want to be a meal for a giant squid. Keiko screamed and moved away from the giant arm, but it kept moving and calling out her name. Keiko woke up shaking and sweating. "What a nightmare! That's the last time I read about a scary animal before I go to sleep!"

1. Which of these could not really happen?
   Ⓐ A girl has a nightmare.
   Ⓑ A giant squid searches for food.
   Ⓒ A giant squid calls out Keiko's name.
   Ⓓ A giant squid roams the deep ocean.

2. How do you know that this story is mostly real?
   Ⓐ Giant squids can speak.
   Ⓑ Giant squids often attack boaters.
   Ⓒ Giant squids really exist.
   Ⓓ Nightmares are about real things.

 Work with a partner. Talk about your answers to questions 1 and 2. Tell why you chose the answers you did.

**Remember:** **Things that could happen in real life are real.**
**Things that could not happen in real life are make-believe.**

★ To figure out if what you are reading is mostly real, ask yourself, "Could all of the events really happen? Do the characters act as they might in real life? Could the setting really exist?"

★ To figure out if what you are reading is mostly make-believe, ask yourself, "Are any of the events unlikely or magical? Do animals talk? Do characters do impossible things?"

**Read this Native American folktale. As you read, ask yourself, "Which parts of the story are mostly make-believe?" Then answer the questions.**

---

### The Quarrel Between Wind and Thunder

Wind said, "On this earth I am the one who keeps everything in good shape. I do all the good work."

"No," said Thunder, "I'm the one who really keeps this world in proper shape."

Thunder was angry. He didn't want to stay with Wind. He went away.

But Wind said, "I don't need him. I'll keep everything on the earth in good shape. I'll make the plants grow."

Wind began to blow. He blew and blew. No plants grew. The earth began to get brown and parched. Everything was drying up. Wind saw that what he had said was not true. He had to go to Thunder.

"I see that I cannot do it alone," he said. "We must work together again. The earth is looking very dry and is all burned up. I want you to come with me again."

So Thunder came back. He made his noise. The rain began to fall. Then the plants began to grow quickly, and the grass got tall. Wind came after Thunder and was glad as he blew among the tall grasses. So this is how these two came together and have been working together ever since.

---

3. Which of these could really happen?
   Ⓐ Thunder makes a noise.
   Ⓑ Thunder gets angry and goes away.
   Ⓒ Wind realizes that he made a mistake.
   Ⓓ Wind and Thunder argue with each other.

4. How do you know that this story is mostly make-believe?
   Ⓐ Wind and thunder don't exist in real life.
   Ⓑ Wind and thunder can't talk.
   Ⓒ The setting does not really exist.
   Ⓓ The earth becomes dry without rain.

Look at the answer choices for each question. Read why each answer choice is correct or not correct.

3. Which of these could really happen?

● Thunder makes a noise.

*This answer is correct because in real life, thunder does make noise. This part of the story is real. It could really happen.*

Ⓑ Thunder gets angry and goes away.

*This answer is not correct because in real life, thunder does not have feelings. It cannot get angry the way a person does. This part of the story is make-believe. It could not really happen.*

Ⓒ Wind realizes that he made a mistake.

*This answer is not correct because in real life, wind cannot think, so it cannot realize it made a mistake. This part of the story is make-believe. It could not really happen.*

Ⓓ Wind and Thunder argue with each other.

*This answer is not correct because in real life, wind and thunder are kinds of weather. They cannot talk or argue the way people do. This part of the story is make-believe. It could not really happen.*

4. How do you know that this story is mostly make-believe?

Ⓐ Wind and thunder don't exist in real life.

*This answer is not correct because wind and thunder do exist in real life. Wind really does blow and can dry up the earth. Thunder really does make a noise and is often followed by rain.*

● Wind and thunder can't talk.

*This answer is correct because wind and thunder can't talk in real life. In the folktale, they talk, they brag, they get angry, and they realize their mistakes.*

Ⓒ The setting does not really exist.

*This answer is not correct because the setting in this story is the earth, and the earth does really exist.*

Ⓓ The earth becomes dry without rain.

*This answer is not correct because in real life, the earth can become dry without rain.*

★ Real stories include autobiographies, biographies, tales of everyday life, news reports, and informational articles.

★ Make-believe stories include fables, fairy tales, folktales, myths, legends, tall tales, and science fiction.

**Read this story from the people of Hawaii. Then answer the questions.**

### The Fire Goddess

Long ago, Pele, the goddess of fire, grew restless. So she set out on the sea in her canoe. She traveled a long way until she came to a chain of lovely islands. The first island she saw was Niihau, where she stayed. Before too long, Pele's sister arrived on Niihau too. Her name was Namaka-o-kiaha`i, and she was the goddess of the sea. Every time Pele created a fire, Namaka-o-kiaha`i sent huge waves to put it out.

Pele escaped by moving on to the next island, Kauai. Here, Pele met Prince Lohi`au. Pele and the prince fell in love. For a short time, Pele was happy, but then Namaka-o-kiaha`i came after her again. Pele kept moving south—to Oahu, Molokai, Lanai, Maui—but her sister always followed her.

Finally, Pele reached the big island of Hawaii. Here, she saw a great mountain volcano that might protect her from her sister. Pele knew that she had finally found her home. She called it Mauna Loa, which means "long mountain."

Pele asked another of her sisters, Hi`iaka, to bring Lohi`au to Mauna Loa. The trip took much longer than expected. By the time Hi`iaka and Lohi`au arrived, Pele was filled with rage. She spit out fire and lava and killed them both. Today, islanders say that when the goddess is happy, all is peaceful and calm. But if someone dares to anger Pele, the earth will tremble and lava will flow as Mauna Loa erupts once more.

5. Which of these could really happen?
   Ⓐ A goddess sends waves to put out fires.
   Ⓑ A mountain is found on the island of Hawaii.
   Ⓒ A volcano erupts when a goddess is angry.
   Ⓓ When a goddess is happy, a volcano is quiet.

6. You can tell this story is mostly make-believe because
   Ⓐ Pele falls in love with a prince.
   Ⓑ Pele travels from island to island in a canoe.
   Ⓒ Pele and her sisters do not get along.
   Ⓓ the characters do impossible things.

7. Which of these could not really happen?
   Ⓐ A trip takes longer than expected.
   Ⓑ Mauna Loa erupts now and then.
   Ⓒ Pele spits out fire and lava.
   Ⓓ Hawaiians tell a story that explains why Mauna Loa erupts.

8. Which of these could not really happen?
   Ⓐ A person moves to Hawaii.
   Ⓑ A chain of islands is found in the ocean.
   Ⓒ A woman causes a volcano to erupt.
   Ⓓ A woman asks a sister for a favor.

**Read this conversation taken from an Internet chat room. Then answer the questions.**

**Jasmine:** Hey, does anyone out there know anything about planets?

**Landru:** Sure. I know a lot about the solar system.

**Jasmine:** I'm doing a science project on Neptune. It's my favorite planet. It's so far away, and I really like its deep blue color.

**Landru:** Actually, it's not so blue up close.

**Jasmine:** Up close? You must be using a really powerful telescope! Is your mom or dad an astronomer or something?

**Landru:** . . . or something.

**Jasmine:** Well, I'd like to go to Neptune someday. Of course, even if I could get there, there would be no way to breathe.

**Landru:** Luckily, I don't have that problem.

**Jasmine:** What do you mean? All human beings have to breathe.

**Landru:** Who said anything about being human?

9. Which of these could really happen?
   Ⓐ Two people chat in an Internet chat room.
   Ⓑ Neptune can be seen up close from Earth.
   Ⓒ People live on Neptune.
   Ⓓ Astronomers can breathe on Neptune.

10. Which of these could not really happen?
   Ⓐ Landru helps Jasmine with her science project.
   Ⓑ Landru knows a lot about the solar system.
   Ⓒ Landru explains facts about Neptune to Jasmine.
   Ⓓ Landru takes Jasmine on a trip to Neptune.

11. Which of these could really happen?
   Ⓐ Landru does not breathe.
   Ⓑ Landru has friends on many planets.
   Ⓒ Jasmine sees Neptune by using a powerful telescope.
   Ⓓ Jasmine travels through the solar system.

12. Which of these could not really happen?
   Ⓐ Jasmine asks Landru for help with her project.
   Ⓑ Landru has seen Neptune up close.
   Ⓒ Landru's parents are astronomers.
   Ⓓ Jasmine learns about the solar system.

 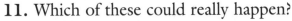

★ A test question about distinguishing between real and make-believe may ask you to tell the difference between things that could happen in real life and things that could not.

★ A test question about distinguishing between real and make-believe often contains the words *could really happen* or *could not really happen*.

Here is a traditional American folk song. Read the lyrics.
Then do Numbers 13 and 14.

### The Train Pulled in the Station

O, the train pulled in the station,
    The bell was ringing wet;
The track ran by the depot,
    And I think it's running yet.

'Twas midnight on the ocean,
    Not a streetcar was in sight;
The sun and moon were shining,
    And it rained all day that night.

'Twas a summer day in winter,
    And the snow was raining fast,
As a barefoot boy, with shoes on,
    Stood, sitting in the grass.

O, I jumped into the river,
    Just because it had a bed;
I took a sheet of water
    For to cover up my head.

O, the rain makes all things beautiful,
    The flower and grasses too;
If the rain makes all things beautiful,
    Why don't it rain on you?

**Distinguishing Between Real and Make-believe**

13. Which of these could really happen?
    Ⓐ It rains all day that night.
    Ⓑ The track runs by the depot.
    Ⓒ It is a summer day in winter.
    Ⓓ A barefoot boy stands sitting in the grass.

**Distinguishing Between Real and Make-believe**

14. Which of these could not really happen?
    Ⓐ Rain makes things beautiful.
    Ⓑ A person jumps into a river.
    Ⓒ Water is used for a sheet.
    Ⓓ A train pulls into a station.

Here is a tall tale about a sailor. Read the tale. Then do Numbers 15 and 16.

### Old Stormalong

Alfred Bulltop Stormalong was famous for his big ways. By age 12, he stood 36 feet tall and had the hunger of 600 men. He ate ostrich eggs for breakfast and drank gallons of soup for lunch. For dinner, he'd eat enough shark to fill a warehouse.

Stormalong was too big to fit in any buildings in his town. So he chose the ocean as his home. "The sailor's life is the only one for me," said he.

Stormalong went to Boston Harbor and climbed aboard the *Lady of the Sea*. It was the biggest clipper ship in the Atlantic Ocean. He spent several years sailing the high seas on the sleek, wind-driven vessel. But he was never truly happy. Every night, he had to sleep in a rowboat by himself. The hammocks on the *Lady* were too small for the giant.

In good time, a ship was finally built that was just right for Stormalong. The *Courser* was the biggest clipper ship in the world. Her sails were so tall that they could touch the sun and the moon. It took 32 seamen just to pilot the wheel. Stormalong, though, could turn the wheel with just his pinkie.

One day, though, a hurricane pushed the *Courser* toward some islands in the Caribbean Sea. Stormalong steered the ship clear of the islands, but then the storm grew fiercer. It drove the mighty *Courser* toward the Isthmus of Panama. The vessel ran right across the land, digging a deep ditch from the Atlantic Ocean on one side to the Pacific Ocean on the other side. That opening is now called the Panama Canal.

Stormalong lived to a ripe old age. Then one fine morning, Old Stormalong drew his last breath of ocean air and was gone. The men of the *Courser* buried the sailor by the shore. There he would always feel the salt spray of the sea.

### Distinguishing Between Real and Make-believe

15. Which of these could really happen?
    - Ⓐ A man is too big to fit in any buildings in his town.
    - Ⓑ A man drinks gallons of soup for lunch.
    - Ⓒ A man lives to a ripe old age.
    - Ⓓ A man grows to be 36 feet tall.

### Distinguishing Between Real and Make-believe

16. Which of these could not really happen?
    - Ⓐ A man becomes a sailor.
    - Ⓑ A man creates the Panama Canal with his ship.
    - Ⓒ A man chooses the ocean as his home.
    - Ⓓ A man is buried by the shore.

## PART ONE: READ A FOLKTALE

Here is an African folktale. Read the folktale.
Then do Numbers 1 through 6.

### Hare, Hippo and Elephant

Hare was a lazy thing. When he got married and settled down, he still couldn't be bothered to work hard. Go out in the fields so that he could feed his wife and himself? Not on your life.

Then one day, he had an idea. He took a long rope and went to find Hippo.

"Hippo, will you listen to me a moment? Why don't we have a game here! I'll tie this rope to you and see if I can pull you out of the mud."

"Sounds like a great game to me," said Hippo, "one I can't lose."

"Good," said Hare. "I'll go off among the trees over there. The moment you feel a tug on the rope, pull like mad, OK? But I'm warning you, I'm pretty strong."

Hippo laughed. "Yes, of course you are, Hare."

Hare tied the rope around Hippo and then went off among the trees and waited. It wasn't long before Elephant came down to the water hole. Hare stopped him. "Oh, Elephant, have you got a moment? I'm looking for someone to challenge me in a tug-of-war. . . . If you win, I'll do anything you want."

Elephant liked the sound of that very much indeed. So he let Hare tie the rope around him. Then off went Hare, telling Elephant to start pulling when he felt a tug on the rope.

Halfway along the rope, where neither Hippo nor Elephant could see him, Hare gave a tug on the rope, first one way and then the other. At once, Elephant and Hippo started heaving on the rope. They heaved all day and all night. The sun came up again, and still they heaved, until they fell down exhausted.

Both animals wondered just how Hare had managed to win. So, after resting, they staggered to their feet and started walking toward each other. When they met, they were furious at Hare for tricking them.

The next day, Hare went out and was rather pleased to see that the ground was all churned up. "Just ready to plant my seeds in," he thought. "And just think, I didn't even have to do any heavy digging and plowing. Won't my wife be pleased with me!"

## Identifying Author's Purpose

1. The author wrote this folktale mainly to
   A entertain readers with a story about a lazy, but clever, hare.
   B persuade readers to feel sorry for Elephant and Hippo.
   C inform readers about farming in Africa.
   D describe how to play the game of tug-of-war.

## Identifying Author's Purpose

2. You know your answer to question 1 is correct because the folktale mainly
   A contains many details that describe something.
   B provides facts or tells readers how to do something.
   C tries to convince readers of something.
   D tells a story that is enjoyable to read.

## Interpreting Figurative Language

3. In the first paragraph, the phrase *not on your life* means
   A "not unless it causes your death."
   B "not unless you put my life in danger."
   C "not for any reason, no matter what."
   D "not while you are still living."

## Interpreting Figurative Language

4. In paragraph five, what does the phrase *pull like mad* mean?
   A "pull as if you are mad"
   B "pull with an angry look on your face"
   C "pull like a crazed animal"
   D "pull as hard as you can"

## Distinguishing Between Real and Make-believe

5. Which of these could really happen?
   A A hare ties a rope around a hippo and an elephant.
   B An elephant calls a hare a little fool.
   C An elephant and a hippo get mad at a hare for tricking them.
   D An elephant comes to the watering hole.

## Distinguishing Between Real and Make-believe

6. How do you know that this folktale is mostly make-believe?
   A Elephants don't like water.
   B The animals act like people.
   C Hippos don't like the mud.
   D Hares, hippos, and elephants don't exist in real life.

Here is a news story about an event that took place in Alaska. Read the news story. Then do Numbers 7 through 12.

## The Arctic News                    January 28, 1925

The people of Nome, Alaska, were in trouble. An illness called diphtheria was sweeping through the town. People were dying, and many more might die soon. Nome needed medicine badly, but the nearest supply was hundreds of miles to the south, in Anchorage. Winter storms raged. No planes could fly. Snow buried the railroad tracks. How could the medicine get from Anchorage to Nome?

Dogsled. That was the only way. Teams of dogs would take turns traveling north like runners in a relay race.

The first team set out pulling their sled loaded with medicine. They traveled many miles and then met up with the second team. The second team took over until it met up with the third team. So it went until an exhausted dog team pulled into a little town just 60 miles south of Nome. The snowstorm was getting wilder by the minute. The temperature was 30 below zero and falling. The man driving the sled couldn't see the nose in front of his face.

The driver of the fresh team was a man named Gunnar Kasson. He decided to take a chance and head out into the deadly storm. He put his smartest dog in the lead, Balto. Part wolf, Balto was the most dependable dog Kasson had ever known. Kasson would not be able to see well enough to steer the sled. He would have to let Balto lead the way.

The trail disappeared under whirling snow. Balto pushed on. The team hauled through sea ice that rumbled and buckled. Balto pushed on. When the ice boomed like thunder and cracked wide open, Balto led the team miles around the water. Hour after hour, Balto pushed on through the freezing storm, through snowdrifts that almost buried them all. He did not let the dogs rest, for resting might mean freezing to death.

At last, Balto led the dogs, Kasson, and the valuable medicine into Nome. Their journey had taken an unbelievable 20 hours.

## Identifying Author's Purpose

7. The author's main purpose in the first paragraph is to
   - (A) describe a situation in Nome, Alaska, one winter.
   - (B) persuade readers that diphtheria is a deadly disease.
   - (C) explain why Nome is often hit hard by storms.
   - (D) delight readers with a story about an amazing dog.

## Identifying Author's Purpose

8. What is the author's purpose in paragraph five?
   - (A) to tell a funny story about a stubborn dog
   - (B) to describe how the dogsled teams took turns traveling north
   - (C) to inform readers about Balto's bravery
   - (D) to convince readers that Balto would become famous

## Interpreting Figurative Language

9. In paragraph two, the writer compares the dog teams to
   - (A) a pack of wolves.
   - (B) runners in a relay race.
   - (C) race-car drivers.
   - (D) fast planes.

## Interpreting Figurative Language

10. Which of these is a simile?
    - (A) most dependable dog
    - (B) sweeping through the town
    - (C) an exhausted dog team
    - (D) boomed like thunder

## Distinguishing Between Real and Make-believe

11. Which of these could really happen?
    - (A) Balto decides to become a doctor.
    - (B) Balto brags about his courage.
    - (C) Balto leads the dog team through a terrible storm.
    - (D) Balto tells the other dogs that they cannot rest.

## Distinguishing Between Real and Make-believe

12. Which of these could not really happen?
    - (A) The temperature hits 30 below zero.
    - (B) Balto's journey takes 20 hours.
    - (C) A winter storm prevents planes from flying.
    - (D) Balto enjoys being the smartest dog on his team.

## PART ONE: READ A TALL TALE

Here is a tall tale about an African-American folk hero.
Read the tall tale. Then do Numbers 1 through 12.

When John Henry was born, he was the most powerful-looking infant anyone had ever seen. He had broad shoulders, and arms as thick as stovepipes. His smile was so bright that it lit up the dark sky.

The mighty child grew faster than the wind. By the time he was ten, he was hammering steel for the railroad. From dawn to dusk, he pounded steel spikes into solid rock with a long-handled hammer, making deep holes. Workers then filled the holes with explosives and blasted the rock away to make tunnels.

By his twenties, John Henry was the best "steel-drivin' man" in the country. His hammer moved as quick as lightning, so he always kept a pail of water nearby just to cool the hammer down. Most of the railroad bosses wanted John Henry to work for them. One boss convinced John Henry to lead the team of steel drivers on the Big Bend Tunnel being built in the Allegheny Mountains of West Virginia.

One day, a fast-talking salesman brought a steam drill to the work site. He boasted that the steam drill could dig holes faster than a dozen men. John Henry looked at that steam drill and thought of all the workers who would lose their jobs to machines. Then he called out, "Well, a man ain't nothin' but a man. But a man's just got to do his best. And before I let a steam drill beat me down, I'd rather die with a hammer in my hand."

So, John Henry entered a race to prove that he could drive a hammer faster than any machine. As he tunneled into the mountain, he hammered faster and faster and harder and harder, until his hammer glowed white-hot, like a burning coal. As he dug deeper and deeper into the tunnel, the crowd outside could still hear that cold steel ring.

When the race was over, John Henry had driven two 7-foot holes into the rock. The steam drill had made only a 9-foot shaft. John Henry beat the steam drill, but he had hammered so hard that his great heart burst. And he laid down his hammer and died.

## Finding Main Idea

1. What is the story mostly about?
   Ⓐ life as a worker on the railroad
   Ⓑ the worries of a steel driver
   Ⓒ a strong man who died doing his best
   Ⓓ a man who could work faster than a machine

## Recalling Facts and Details

2. John Henry began working for the railroad when he was
   Ⓐ an infant.
   Ⓑ ten years old.
   Ⓒ seven years old.
   Ⓓ in his twenties.

## Understanding Sequence

3. The boxes tell some things that happened in the story.

| John Henry first saw the steam drill. | | John Henry entered a race against the steam drill. |
|---|---|---|
| 1 | 2 | 3 |

   What belongs in box 2?
   Ⓐ John Henry accepted a job working on the Big Bend Tunnel.
   Ⓑ John Henry's great heart burst.
   Ⓒ John Henry thought of all the workers who would lose their jobs.
   Ⓓ John Henry was the best "steel-driving' man" in the country.

## Recognizing Cause and Effect

4. Because his hammer moved so fast,
   Ⓐ John Henry was always racing against the other steel drivers.
   Ⓑ John Henry always kept a pail of water nearby to cool it down.
   Ⓒ John Henry developed broad shoulders and thick arms.
   Ⓓ John Henry was challenged to a race against a steam drill.

## Comparing and Contrasting

5. How was John Henry different from the other steel drivers?
   Ⓐ He was the only one hired to work on the Big Bend Tunnel.
   Ⓑ He was the only one who could tunnel into a mountain.
   Ⓒ He hammered steel into rock, but they used explosives.
   Ⓓ He was faster and more powerful than they were.

## Making Predictions

6. Predict what might have happened if John Henry had lived longer.
   Ⓐ He would have become too proud.
   Ⓑ He would have gotten tired of his job.
   Ⓒ He would have continued to work hard.
   Ⓓ He would have been replaced by a machine.

## Finding Word Meaning in Context

7. In the last paragraph, the word *shaft* means
   - Ⓐ "an arrow or a spear."
   - Ⓑ "a ray or a beam."
   - Ⓒ "a tall, narrow passage sunk into the earth."
   - Ⓓ "the space where an elevator is housed."

## Identifying Author's Purpose

10. The author probably wrote the story to
    - Ⓐ describe steam drills.
    - Ⓑ explain how railroad tunnels are made.
    - Ⓒ persuade readers to support workers' rights.
    - Ⓓ entertain readers with a story about a folk hero.

## Drawing Conclusions and Making Inferences

8. From the story, you can tell that John Henry
   - Ⓐ was not very sure of himself.
   - Ⓑ acted without thinking.
   - Ⓒ was in poor health.
   - Ⓓ was brave and determined.

## Interpreting Figurative Language

11. In paragraph five, the phrase *as quick as lightning* means that John Henry's hammer
    - Ⓐ made deep holes.
    - Ⓑ moved quickly.
    - Ⓒ was too hot to hold.
    - Ⓓ was stronger than metal.

## Distinguishing Between Fact and Opinion

9. Which of these is an opinion about John Henry?
   - Ⓐ He was the most powerful-looking infant anyone had ever seen.
   - Ⓑ Most of the railroad bosses wanted him to work for them.
   - Ⓒ He could drive a hammer faster than a steam drill.
   - Ⓓ He swung a hammer hard and fast.

## Distinguishing Between Real and Make-believe

12. Which of these could not really happen?
    - Ⓐ John Henry works from dawn to dusk.
    - Ⓑ John Henry hammers so fast that his hammer glows white-hot.
    - Ⓒ A fast-talking salesman boasts about the job a steam drill can do.
    - Ⓓ The crowd hears the cold steel ring as John Henry digs into the tunnel.

Here is an article about the history of numbers. Read the article.
Then do Numbers 13 through 24.

You are used to writing numerals. So you may not realize that numerals had to be invented. The early Egyptians invented one of the first number systems, about 5,000 years ago. They based their system on the number ten, probably because it equaled the number of fingers on both hands. The Egyptians used symbols to stand for numbers. Each symbol stood for its given value. For example, ∩ meant 10, ∩∩ meant 20, and so on. Egyptian numbers could be written and read from right to left, left to right, or up and down. The order of the symbols did not matter.

The ancient Chinese also developed a number system using base ten. They, however, showed numbers with small sticks. Where the sticks were put determined a number's value. For example, ⊤≡∥ was 637, but ∥≡⊤ was 736.

The ancient Romans chose letters to stand for numbers. They based their number system on five. The letters I, II, and III stood for 1, 2, and 3. The letters V, X, L, C, D, and M stood for 5, 10, 50, 100, 500, and 1,000. The letters were read in order from left to right. When a Roman numeral that is the same size or smaller comes after another Roman numeral, their values are added together. Thus, VI is (5 + 1), or 6, and XX is (10 + 10), or 20. When a Roman numeral that is smaller comes right before a larger numeral, the lower number is subtracted from the higher one. For example, IV is (5 − 1), or 4, and XL is (50 − 10), or 40.

The Hindus of India figured out that they could use just nine symbols (1–9) to represent all numbers. The placement of each symbol set its value. Thus, it was possible to write a huge number, such as 895,673,421, without using up a lot of space. The Hindus also invented the symbol 0. Its place among numerals makes a difference in the value shown by the numerals. The Hindus taught their ten numerals to Arab traders, who then introduced them to Europe. When the Europeans came to America in the 1600s, they brought the Arabic numerals with them. These are the numerals we use today.

## Finding Main Idea

**13.** The best title for this article is
   Ⓐ "Letters for Numbers."
   Ⓑ "Why Zero Was Invented."
   Ⓒ "The First Number System."
   Ⓓ "The History of Numbers."

## Recalling Facts and Details

**14.** Who invented Arabic numerals?
   Ⓐ Arabs
   Ⓑ Hindus
   Ⓒ Europeans
   Ⓓ Americans

## Understanding Sequence

**15.** Which type of number system came last?
   Ⓐ one in which each symbol stood for its given value
   Ⓑ one that used the symbol 0 to show place value
   Ⓒ one that used stick arrangements to determine value
   Ⓓ one based on the number five

## Recognizing Cause and Effect

**16.** The Egyptians based their number system on ten because
   Ⓐ it equaled the number of a person's fingers and toes.
   Ⓑ they didn't know about the Roman number system.
   Ⓒ it equaled the number of fingers on both hands.
   Ⓓ it was easy to show the number ten with sticks.

## Comparing and Contrasting

**17.** How were the Egyptian and the Chinese number systems alike?
   Ⓐ Both were based on the number ten.
   Ⓑ Both showed numbers with sticks.
   Ⓒ Numbers in both systems were read only from left to right.
   Ⓓ Letters stood for numbers in both systems.

## Making Predictions

**18.** Predict how life would be different today if there were no numerals.
   Ⓐ People would not be able to farm, fish, or hunt.
   Ⓑ People would not be able to communicate with each other.
   Ⓒ People would have different ways of adding, measuring, and estimating.
   Ⓓ People would have to depend more on the kindness of others.

## Finding Word Meaning in Context

19. In paragraph four, the best meaning of the word *represent* is
    - Ⓐ "to take up space."
    - Ⓑ "to invent something new."
    - Ⓒ "to speak or act for someone else."
    - Ⓓ "to stand for something."

## Identifying Author's Purpose

22. What is the author's main purpose for writing the article?
    - Ⓐ to describe our present number system
    - Ⓑ to tell readers about different number systems
    - Ⓒ to persuade readers to learn more about other number systems
    - Ⓓ to entertain readers with details about other cultures

## Drawing Conclusions and Making Inferences

20. From this article, you can tell that
    - Ⓐ the Hindus' number system was simpler than other systems.
    - Ⓑ Roman numerals are no longer used.
    - Ⓒ the Chinese used hundreds of sticks to show numbers.
    - Ⓓ letters are easier to draw than symbols.

## Interpreting Figurative Language

23. In the last paragraph, what does the phrase *figured out* mean?
    - Ⓐ "drew a shape or design"
    - Ⓑ "solved a math problem"
    - Ⓒ "understood something"
    - Ⓓ "found out what something was worth"

## Distinguishing Between Fact and Opinion

21. Which of these is a fact?
    - Ⓐ The Egyptians weren't good at keeping numbers in order.
    - Ⓑ The Chinese stick arrangement was too complicated.
    - Ⓒ The Romans' number system was the best.
    - Ⓓ The Hindus used nine symbols and 0 for larger numbers.

## Distinguishing Between Real and Make-believe

24. Which of these could not really happen?
    - Ⓐ Numbers take the place of all words.
    - Ⓑ Romans develop a number system based on five.
    - Ⓒ Ancient stick arrangements are found in China.
    - Ⓓ Arab traders teach Europeans a new number system.

Here is a book report about an important Native-American woman.
Read the book report. Then do Numbers 25 through 36.

The biography *The Bird Woman* is about the most remarkable Native-American woman I've ever learned about. Her name was Sacajawea. After reading this book, I feel as if I've gotten to know this brave woman.

The story begins with Sacajawea's birth. She was born some time around 1788. She lived among the Shoshone in what is now Idaho. When Sacajawea was only four years old, an enemy tribe captured her. Her kidnappers took her to the area that is now North Dakota. There, Sacajawea was sold to a French-Canadian trapper named Toussaint Charbonneau. He became her husband when Sacajawea was 16.

Sacajawea and Charbonneau were staying at Fort Mandan in North Dakota. There, they met Meriwether Lewis and William Clark in 1804. President Thomas Jefferson had hired Lewis and Clark to explore the Louisiana Territory. The United States had just bought this huge parcel of land from France. The Lewis and Clark expedition consisted of over 40 men. They started their journey in St. Louis, Missouri. They hoped to find a water route across the Rocky Mountains to the Pacific Ocean.

Lewis and Clark asked Charbonneau to join their expedition as a guide. Sacajawea wanted to see the "Big Waters," her name for the Pacific. She was the only woman to join the expedition. She carried her newborn baby boy on her back as they traveled. The explorers faced grizzly bears, steep cliffs, and fierce rapids. Sacajawea proved to be a valuable member of the group. She taught the men which plants could be used for medicine, and she made buckskin clothes for them. She also helped them communicate with Native Americans.

When Lewis and Clark reached the Rockies, they realized that they could not continue their journey by water. Things began to look up, though, when they met a group of Shoshone led by Sacajawea's long-lost brother. Sacajawea persuaded her brother to trade with the explorers for the horses they needed.

Sacajawea stayed with the expedition all the way to the Pacific Ocean and partway home. Sacajawea died when she was only 26. Her life was short, but her name lives on as an important woman in history.

## Finding Main Idea

**25.** What is the book report mostly about?
- (A) famous explorers
- (B) the Louisiana Territory
- (C) a Native American heroine
- (D) the Lewis and Clark expedition

## Recalling Facts and Details

**26.** Where did Sacajawea meet Lewis and Clark?
- (A) Idaho
- (B) Missouri
- (C) North Dakota
- (D) Louisiana

## Understanding Sequence

**27.** What happened immediately after Sacajawea was captured?
- (A) She married Toussaint Charbonneau.
- (B) She was sold to a French-Canadian trapper.
- (C) She met Lewis and Clark.
- (D) She was taken to the area that is now North Dakota.

## Recognizing Cause and Effect

**28.** Which of these is not a reason that Sacajawea was important to the expedition?
- (A) She helped the men communicate with Native Americans.
- (B) She had a baby boy with her.
- (C) She taught the men which plants could be used for medicine.
- (D) She made buckskin clothes for the men.

## Comparing and Contrasting

**29.** What was one major difference between Sacajawea and the other explorers?
- (A) She was the only one who was married.
- (B) She was the only one who was a woman.
- (C) She was the only valuable member of the group.
- (D) She was the only one who knew the way across the Rockies.

## Making Predictions

**30.** What might have happened if the expedition hadn't met the Shoshone?
- (A) The group would have starved to death.
- (B) The journey west would have been even more difficult.
- (C) Other Native Americans would have gladly helped the explorers.
- (D) Sacajawea would never have known that she was kidnapped as a child.

## Finding Word Meaning in Context

31. In paragraph three, the word *expedition* means
    - (A) "a short trip to do something fun."
    - (B) "a special vacation out West."
    - (C) "a group making a long trip, usually for exploring."
    - (D) "quickness."

## Identifying Author's Purpose

34. Paragraph two was written mainly to
    - (A) describe life in the early 1800s.
    - (B) encourage readers to read about famous Native Americans.
    - (C) entertain readers with tales about Lewis and Clark.
    - (D) inform readers about Sacajawea's early life.

## Drawing Conclusions and Making Inferences

32. From this book report, you can tell that the reviewer
    - (A) considers Sacajawea a hero.
    - (B) feels sorry for Sacajawea.
    - (C) is interested in the history of Native-American people.
    - (D) believes the expedition was poorly planned.

## Interpreting Figurative Language

35. In paragraph five, the phrase *things began to look up* means that
    - (A) the expedition was nearing the top of the Rockies.
    - (B) the explorers had respect for the Shoshone.
    - (C) conditions were improving for the explorers.
    - (D) the explorers saw many birds flying overhead.

## Distinguishing Between Fact and Opinion

33. Which of these is an opinion about Sacajawea?
    - (A) She had a short life.
    - (B) She was a famous Native-American woman.
    - (C) She went on the journey shortly after giving birth.
    - (D) She was the most remarkable Native-American woman.

## Distinguishing Between Real and Make-believe

36. Which of these could not really happen?
    - (A) Sacajawea persuades her brother to trade for horses.
    - (B) Sacajawea marries at age 16.
    - (C) Sacajawea travels with a baby boy.
    - (D) Sacajawea is part bird and part woman.

# ACKNOWLEDGMENTS

Curriculum Associates wishes to thank the following authors and publishers for their permission to reprint copyrighted material. Every effort has been made to locate all copyright holders. Any errors or omissions in copyright notice are inadvertent and will be credited in future printings as they are discovered.

page 62:    "I Don't Like It" by Jeffie Ross Gordon. Reprinted with permission of Judith Ross Enderlee and Stephanie Jacob Gordon.

page 103:   "The Popcorn Patch" from *Tall Tales from the High Hills and Other Stories* by Ellis Credle. Copyright 1957 by Ellis Credle.

page 106:   "The Quarrel Between Wind and Thunder" from *Myths and Legends of Lipan Apache* by Morris Edward Opler. Copyright 1940 by J. J. Augustin, Inc. Reprinted by permission of J. J. Augustin, Inc.

page 112:   "Hare, Hippo and Elephant" from *SOUTH AND NORTH, EAST AND WEST* Edited text ©1992 Michael Rosen. Reproduced by permission of Walker Books ltd., London. Published in the US by Candlewick Press Inc., Cambridge, MA.

## Illustration Credits

LuAnn Graham
Susan Hawk/pages 30, 77, 106, and 116
Lisa Gollihue/pages 105 and 112

## Photography Credits

www.arttoday.com/pages 4, 5, 25, 32, 67, 72, 75, 78, 86, 90, 95, 114, and 122
Courtesy of Winchester House, San Jose, CA/page 37
Archive Photos/page 53
NASA/page 65
Corbis/page 80
Courtesy of Johnson Space Center/page 83

**Developer and Writer:** Joan Krensky

**Editor:** Deborah Adcock

**Designer:** Jamie Ruh